Discovering
Advanced
Algebra
An Investigative Approach

SECOND EDITION

Investigation Worksheets

DISCOVERING

MATHEMATICS™

Key Curriculum Press
Innovators in Mathematics Education

Editor: Sharon Taylor

Project Administrator: Tamar Wolins

Production Editor: Christa Edwards

Editorial Production Supervisor: Kristin Ferraioli

Production Director: Christine Osborne

Senior Production Coordinator: Ann Rothenbuhler

Text Designer: ICC Macmillan Inc.

Composition, Technical Art: ICC Macmillan Inc.

Cover Designer: Jeff Williams

Printer: Versa Press, Inc.

Textbook Product Manager: Tim Pope

Executive Editor: Josephine Noah

Publisher: Steven Rasmussen

Key Curriculum Press
1150 65th Street
Emeryville, CA 94608
510-595-7000
editorial@keypress.com
www.keypress.com

Printed in the United States of America
10 9 8 7 6 5 4 3 2 1   13 12 11 10 09   ISBN: 978-1-60440-015-1

Contents

Introduction

Many of the key ideas in *Discovering Advanced Algebra* are developed through group investigations done in class. The investigations pose a variety of hands-on tasks for students: taking measurements, collecting data, making calculations, and writing explanations and conclusions. It is important that data and results are easy to read, organized, and accurate so that the concepts and conclusions are clear and so that students can share their results with each other.

These classroom-ready worksheets, provided for every *Discovering Advanced Algebra* investigation, are designed to help your students stay organized as they work through investigation steps. (They can also be used to help absent students make up lessons they miss.) Each worksheet includes all of the steps and questions from the textbook investigation, with space for students to record their work and answers. Where appropriate, worksheets provide blank tables for recording data, blank number lines and graph grids for representing data and graphs, and other useful diagrams. The *Discovering Advanced Algebra Teacher's Edition* references the investigation worksheets in the Resources section at the beginning of each chapter and in the Materials list at the beginning of each lesson that has an investigation.

Investigation Worksheets provides alternate versions of worksheets to accommodate classrooms that don't have access to the materials needed for some investigations, or that need to save time by skipping data-gathering. These worksheets—designated "With Sample Data" or "Without Motion Sensors"—allow your students to experience the investigation discoveries and analysis even if they don't perform all of the investigation procedures. There is one "Supplemental" investigation, provided for Lesson 12.1; if your students do not have a solid understanding of trigonometric ratios, this worksheet can be used for reinforcement before you assign the textbook investigation.

If you have TI-Connect, TI-Nspire Computer Link software, TI-Nspire Connect-To-Class, or TI-Nspire Navigator, and access to a computer, you can take advantage of the calculator sample data files for the TI-83/84 Plus and TI-Nspire provided with the Teaching Resources package. These data sets can be found on the Teaching Resources CD, or at *www.keymath.com/DAA* (for students) or *www.keypress.com/keyonline* (for teachers). You can download documents containing data from the CD or websites to a computer, and from there onto a calculator. Students can then link calculators to transfer files from one calculator to another.

Investigation • Polar Bear Crossing the Arctic

Name _____ Period _____ Date _____

A polar bear rests by a stack of 3000 pounds of fish he has caught. He plans to travel 1000 miles across the Arctic to bring as many fish as possible to his family. He can pull a sled that holds up to 1000 pounds of fish, but he must eat 1 pound of fish at every mile to keep his energy up.

What is the maximum amount of fish (in pounds) the polar bear can transport across the Arctic? How does he do it? Work as a group and prepare a written or visual solution.

Next 1000 miles

Investigation • Problems, Problems, Problems

Name _____ **Period** _____ **Date** _____

Select one of the problems below, and use these four steps to find a solution.

Step 1   List the unknown quantities, and assign a variable to each quantity.

Step 2   Write one or more equations that relate the unknown quantities to conditions of the problem.

Step 3   Solve the equations to find a value for each variable.

Step 4   Interpret your solution according to the context of the problem.

When you finish, write a paragraph answering this question: Which of the four problem-solving steps was hardest for you? Why?

Discovering Advanced Algebra Investigation Worksheets
©2010 Key Curriculum Press

Problem 1

On Monday the manager scheduled two clerks and one supervisor for 8-hour shifts. She was pleased because she met the daily salary budget.

On Tuesday the manager needed two clerks for 8 hours, a third clerk for 4 hours, and one supervisor for 4 hours. She was very pleased to be $10 under budget.

On Wednesday she needed three clerks for 8 hours and one supervisor for 4 hours. This day she was over budget by $20.

All of the clerks make the same hourly wage. What is the daily salary budget?

Problem 2

Sandy uses a $\frac{1}{2}$-ton pickup (a truck that can carry 1000 pounds) to transport ingredients for mortar. Sand comes in 50-pound bags and cement comes in 40-pound bags. Mortar is made from five bags of sand for every bag of cement. How many bags of each should Sandy load to make the most mortar possible?

Investigation • Who Owns the Zebra?

Name _____ Period _____ Date _____

There are five houses along one side of Birch Street, each of a different color. The home-owners each drive a different car, and each has a different pet. The owners all read a different newspaper and plant only one thing in their garden.

- The family with the station wagon lives in the red house.
- The owner of the SUV has a dog.
- The family with the van reads the *Gazette*.
- The green house is immediately to the left of the white house.
- The *Chronicle* is delivered to the green house.
- The man who plants zucchini has birds.
- In the yellow house they plant corn.
- In the middle house they read the *Times*.
- The compact car parks at the first house.
- The family that plants eggplant lives in the house next to the house with cats.
- In the house next to the house where they have a horse, they plant corn.
- The woman who plants beets receives the *Daily News*.
- The owner of the sports car plants okra.
- The family with the compact car lives next to the blue house.
- They read the *Bulletin* in the house next to the house where they plant eggplant.

Who owns the zebra?

Discovering Advanced Algebra Investigation Worksheets
©2010 Key Curriculum Press

Investigation • Monitoring Inventory

Name _____ Period _____ Date _____

Art Smith has been providing the prints of an engraving to FineArt Gallery. He plans to make just 2000 more prints. FineArt has already received 470 of Art's prints. The Little Print Shoppe also wishes to order prints. Art agrees to supply FineArt with 40 prints each month and Little Print Shoppe with 10 prints each month until he runs out.

Step 1 As a group, model what happens to the number of unmade prints, the number of prints delivered to FineArt, and the number delivered to Little Print Shoppe in a **spreadsheet** like the one below. [▶🖵 See **Calculator Note 1C** for different ways to create this table or spreadsheet on your calculator. ◀]

Month	Unmade Prints	FineArt	Little Print Shoppe
1	2000	470	0
2			
. . .			

Step 2 Use your table from Step 1 to answer these questions:

a. How many months will it be until FineArt has an equal number or a greater number of prints than the number of prints left unmade?

b. How many prints will have been delivered to the Little Print Shoppe when FineArt has received twice the number of prints that remain to be made?

Step 3 Write a short summary of how you modeled the number of prints and how you found the answers to the questions in Step 2. Compare your methods with the methods of other groups.

Investigation • Looking for the Rebound

Name_____ Period_____ Date_____

You will need: a ball, a motion sensor

When you drop a ball, the rebound height becomes smaller after each bounce. In this investigation you will write a recursive formula for the height of a real ball as it bounces.

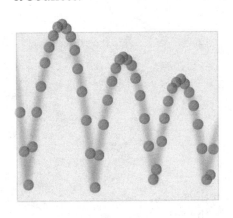

Step 1 Set up your calculator and motion sensor and follow the Procedure Note to collect bouncing-ball data.

[▶ 🖳 See **Calculator Note 1D** for calculator instructions on how to gather data. ◀]

Step 2 The data transferred to your calculator are in the form (x, y), where x is the time since you pressed the trigger, and y is the height of the ball. Trace the data graphed by your calculator to find the starting height and the rebound height after each bounce. Record your data in the table.

Bounce number	Rebound height (m)	Bounce number	Rebound height (m)
0		5	
1		6	
2		7	
3		8	
4		9	

> ## Procedure Note
>
> **Collecting Data**
> 1. Hold the motion sensor above the ball.
> 2. Press the trigger, then release the ball.
> 3. If the ball drifts, try to follow it and maintain the same height with the motion sensor.
> 4. If you do not capture at least 6 good consecutive bounces, repeat the procedure.

Investigation • Looking for the Rebound (continued)

Step 3   Graph a scatter plot of points in the form (*bounce number, rebound height*). Record the graphing window you use. [▶ 🖳 See **Calculator Notes 1E, 1F, 1G** , and **1H** to learn how to enter, plot, trace, and share data. ◀]

Step 4   Compute the rebound ratio for consecutive bounces.

$$rebound\ ratio = \frac{rebound\ height}{previous\ rebound\ height}$$

Step 5   Decide on a single value that best represents the rebound ratio for your ball. Use this ratio to write a recursive formula that models your sequence of *rebound height* data, and use it to generate the first six terms.

Step 6   Compare your experimental data to the terms generated by your recursive formula. How close are they? Describe some of the factors that might affect this experiment. For example, how might the formula change if you used a different kind of ball?

Investigation • Looking for the Rebound

With Sample Data

Name_____ **Period**_____ **Date**_____

When you drop a ball, the rebound height becomes smaller after each bounce. In this investigation you will write a recursive formula for the height of a ball as it bounces.

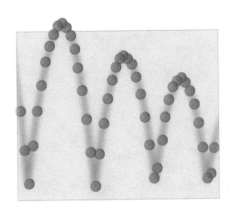

Step 1 A group of students set up their calculator and motion sensor and followed the Procedure Note to collect bouncing-ball data. [▶🖥 See **Calculator Note 1D** for calculator instructions on how to gather data. ◀]

Step 2 The data were transferred to the calculator in the form (x, y), where x is the time since they pressed the trigger, and y is the height of the ball. They traced the data graphed by the calculator to find the starting height and the rebound height after each bounce. These data were recorded in the table.

> **Procedure Note**
>
> **Collecting Data**
> 1. Hold the motion sensor above the ball.
> 2. Press the trigger, then release the ball.
> 3. If the ball drifts, try to follow it and maintain the same height with the motion sensor.
> 4. If you do not capture at least 6 good consecutive bounces, repeat the procedure.

Bounce number	Rebound height (m)	Bounce number	Rebound height (m)
0	1.081	5	0.166
1	0.830	6	0.119
2	0.578	7	0.084
3	0.377	8	0.064
4	0.245	9	0.059

Step 3   Graph a scatter plot of points in the form (*bounce number, rebound height*). Record the graphing window you use. [▶ 🔲 See **Calculator Notes** 1E, 1F, 1G, and 1H to learn how to enter, plot, trace, and share data. ◀]

Step 4   Compute the rebound ratio for consecutive bounces.

$$\text{rebound ratio} = \frac{\text{rebound height}}{\text{previous rebound height}}$$

Step 5   Decide on a single value that best represents the rebound ratio for the ball. Use this ratio to write a recursive formula that models the sequence of *rebound height* data, and use it to generate the first six terms.

Step 6   Compare the experimental data to the terms generated by your recursive formula. How close are they? Describe some of the factors that might affect this experiment. For example, how might the formula change if a different kind of ball was used?

Discovering Advanced Algebra Investigation Worksheets
©2010 Key Curriculum Press

Investigation • Doses of Medicine

Name _____ **Period** _____ **Date** _____

You will need (optional): a bowl, a supply of water, a supply of tinted liquid, measuring cups graduated in milliliters, a sink or waste bucket

Our kidneys continuously filter our blood, removing impurities. Doctors take this into account when prescribing the dosage and frequency of medicine.

In this investigation you will simulate what happens in the body when a patient takes medicine. To represent the blood in a patient's body, use a bowl containing a total of 1 liter (L) of liquid. Start with 16 milliliters (mL) of tinted liquid to represent a dose of medicine in the blood, and use clear water for the rest.

Step 1 Suppose a patient's kidneys filter out 25% of this medicine each day. To simulate this, remove $\frac{1}{4}$, or 250 mL, of the mixture from the bowl and replace it with 250 mL of clear water to represent filtered blood. Use the table to record the amount of medicine in the blood over several days. Repeat the simulation for each day.

Day	Amount of medicine (mL)
0	16
1	
2	
3	
...	

Step 2 Write a recursive formula that generates the sequence in your table.

Step 3 How many days will pass before there is less than 1 mL of medicine in the blood?

Step 4 Is the medicine ever completely removed from the blood? Why or why not?

Step 5   Sketch a graph and describe what happens in the long run.

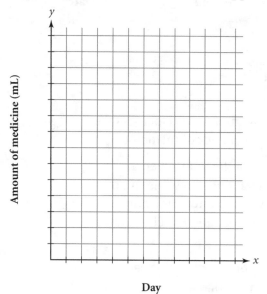

A single dose of medicine is often not enough to treat a patient's condition. Doctors prescribe regular doses to produce and maintain a high enough level of medicine in the body. Next you will modify your simulation to look at what happens when a patient takes medicine daily over a period of time.

Step 6   Start over with 1 L of liquid. Again, all of the liquid is clear water, representing the blood, except for 16 mL of tinted liquid to represent the initial dose of medicine. Each day, 250 mL of liquid is removed and replaced with 234 mL of clear water and 16 mL of tinted liquid to represent a new dose of medicine. Complete this table, recording the amount of medicine in the blood over several days.

Day	Amount of medicine (mL)
0	16
1	
2	
3	
...	

Step 7   Write a recursive formula that generates this sequence.

Step 8   Do the contents of the bowl ever turn into pure medicine? Why or why not?

Step 9   Sketch a graph and explain what happens to the level of medicine in the blood after many days.

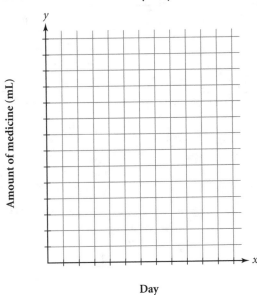

Investigation • Match Them Up

Name_____ **Period**_____ **Date**_____

Match each table with a recursive formula and a graph that represent the same sequence. Write your matches in the blanks. Think about similarities and differences between the sequences and how those similarities and differences affect the tables, formulas, and graphs.

1. _____   **2.** _____   **3.** _____   **4.** _____   **5.** _____   **6.** _____

n	u_n
0	8
1	4
3	1
6	0.125
9	0.015625

n	u_n
0	0.5
1	1
2	2
3	4
4	8

n	u_n
0	-2
1	1
2	2.5
4	3.625
5	3.8125

n	u_n
0	-2
2	2
5	8
7	12
10	18

n	u_n
0	8
1	6
3	2
5	-2
7	-6

n	u_n
0	-4
1	-4
2	-4
4	-4
8	-4

A. $u_0 = 8$
$u_n = u_{n-1} - 2$ where $n \geq 1$

B. $u_0 = 8$
$u_n = 0.5u_{n-1}$ where $n \geq 1$

C. $u_0 = 0.5$
$u_n = 2u_{n-1}$ where $n \geq 1$

D. $u_0 = -2$
$u_n = u_{n-1} + 2$ where $n \geq 1$

E. $u_0 = -4$
$u_n = u_{n-1}$ where $n \geq 1$

F. $u_0 = -2$
$u_n = 0.5u_{n-1} + 2$
where $n \geq 1$

i.
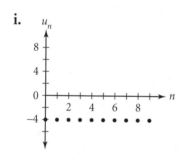

ii.
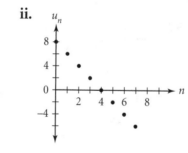

iii.
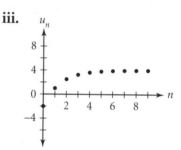

iv.
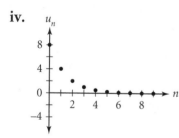

v.
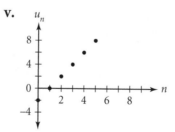

vi.
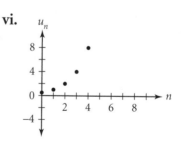

Discovering Advanced Algebra Investigation Worksheets
©2010 Key Curriculum Press

Investigation • Match Them Up (continued)

Write a paragraph that summarizes the relationships between different types of sequences, recursive formulas, and graphs. What generalizations can you make? What do you notice about the shapes of the graphs created from arithmetic and geometric sequences?

Investigation • Life's Big Expenditures

Name_____ **Period**_____ **Date**_____

In this investigation you will use recursion to explore loan balances and payment options. Your calculator will be a helpful tool for trying different sequence models.

Part 1

You plan to borrow $22,000 from a bank to purchase a new car. You will make a payment every month to the bank to repay the loan, and the loan must be paid off in 5 years (60 months). The bank charges interest at an annual rate of 7.9%, compounded monthly. Part of each monthly payment is applied to the interest, and the remainder reduces the starting balance, or principal.

Step 1 What is the *monthly* interest rate? What is the first month's interest on the $22,000? If you make a payment of $300 at the end of the first month, then what is the remaining balance?

Step 2 Record the balances for the first 6 months with monthly payments of $300. How many months will it take to pay off the loan?

Month	Balance
1	
2	
3	
4	
5	
6	

Discovering Advanced Algebra Investigation Worksheets
©2010 Key Curriculum Press

Step 3 Experiment with other values for the monthly payment. What monthly payment allows you to pay off the loan in exactly 60 months?

Step 4 How much do you actually pay for the car using the monthly payment you found in Step 3? (*Hint:* The last payment should be a little less than the other 59 payments.)

Part 2

Use the techniques that you discovered in Part 1 to find the monthly payment for a 30-year home mortgage of $146,000 with an annual interest rate of 7.25%, compounded monthly. How much do you actually pay for the house?

Month	Balance
1	
2	
3	
4	
5	
6	

Investigation • Pulse Rates

Name _____ Period _____ Date _____

You will need: a watch or clock with a second hand

Pulse rate is often used as a measure of whether or not a person is in good physical condition. In this investigation you will practice making box plots, compare box plots, and draw some conclusions about pulse rates.

Step 1 Measure and record your resting pulse for 15 s. Multiply this value by 4 to get the number of beats per minute. Pool data from the entire class.

Step 2 Exercise for 2 min by doing jumping jacks or by running in place. Afterward, measure and record your exercise pulse rate. Pool your data.

Step 3 Order each set of data. Calculate the five-number summaries for your class's resting pulse rates and for your exercise pulse rates.

Ordered resting pulse rates

Ordered exercising pulse rates

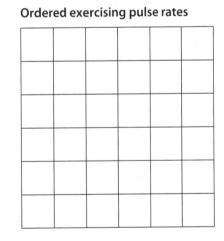

Step 4   Prepare a box plot of the resting pulse rates and a box plot of the exercise pulse rates. Determine a range suitable for displaying both of these graphs on this single axis.

Step 5   Draw conclusions about pulse rates by comparing these two graphs. Be sure to compare not only centers but also spreads and shapes. Could your conclusion apply to a larger population? Describe the population and explain how your class is representative of that population.

Discovering Advanced Algebra Investigation Worksheets
©2010 Key Curriculum Press

Investigation • Pulse Rates

Name _____ **Period** _____ **Date** _____

Pulse rate is often used as a measure of whether or not a person is in good physical condition. In this investigation you will practice making box plots, compare box plots, and draw some conclusions about pulse rates.

Step 1   The students in a mathematics class recorded their resting pulse rates to determine the number of beats per minutes. They pooled their results in this data set.

{68, 76, 84, 80, 76, 72, 60, 68, 68, 80, 68, 80, 64, 64, 72, 76, 72, 68, 56, 88, 80, 76, 68, 56, 64, 60, 92, 72, 84, 72}

Step 2   The students then exercised for 2 min by doing jumping jacks or by running in place. Afterward, they measured their exercise pulse rates and pooled the results in this data set.

{148, 136, 157, 151, 121, 139, 137, 129, 127, 129, 155, 141, 133, 153, 161, 153, 127, 135, 144, 146, 136, 131, 133, 159, 127, 142, 133, 150, 164, 161}

Step 3   Order each set of data. Calculate the five-number summaries for the class's resting pulse rates and for their exercise pulse rates.

Ordered resting pulse rates

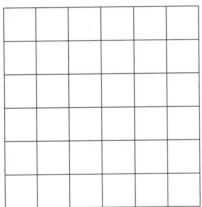

Ordered exercising pulse rates

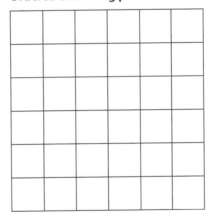

Step 4   Prepare a box plot of the resting pulse rates and a box plot of the
exercise pulse rates. Determine a range suitable for displaying both
of these graphs on this single axis.

Step 5   Draw conclusions about pulse rates by comparing these two
graphs. Be sure to compare not only centers but also spreads
and shapes. Could your conclusion apply to a larger population?
Describe the population and explain how your class is
representative of that population.

Discovering Advanced Algebra Investigation Worksheets
©2010 Key Curriculum Press

Investigation • A Good Design

Name _____ **Period** _____ **Date** _____

You will need: a measuring tape or metersticks, paper, books,
a pad of paper or cardboard, a rubber band, a ruler

In a well-designed experiment, you should be able to follow a specific procedure and get very similar results every time you perform the experiment. In this investigation you will attempt to control the setup of an experiment in order to limit the variability of your results.

Select and perform one of these experiments. Make complete and careful notes about the setup of your experiment.

Experiment 1: Rolling Ball

In this experiment you'll roll a ball of paper down a ramp and off the edge of your desk. Build your ramp from books, notebooks, or a pad of paper. Select the height and slope of your ramp and the distance from the edge of your desk, and determine any other factors that might affect your results. Make a ball by crumpling a piece of paper, and roll it down the ramp. Record the horizontal distance to the place where the ball hits the floor. Repeat this procedure with the same ball, the same ramp setup, and the same release another seven or eight times.

Rolling Ball Data

Distance (cm)									

Experiment 2: Rubber Band Launch

In this experiment you'll use a ruler to launch a rubber band. Select the height and angle of your launch and the length of your stretch, and determine any other factors that might affect your results. Launch the rubber band into an area clear of obstructions. Record the horizontal distance of the flight. Repeat this procedure as precisely as you can with the same rubber band, the same launch setup, and the same stretch another seven or eight times.

Rubber Band Data

Distance (cm)								

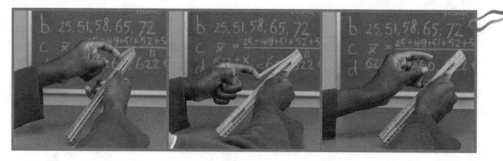

Step 1   Use your data from Experiment 1 or 2. Calculate the mean distance for your trials and then calculate the deviations.

Step 2   In general, how much do your data values differ from the mean? How does the variability in your results relate to how controlled your setup was? Determine a way to calculate a *single* value that tells how accurate your group was at repeating the procedure. Write a formula to calculate your statistic using the deviations.

Investigation • A Good Design (continued)

Step 3 A value known as the **standard deviation** helps measure the spread of data away from the mean. Use your calculator to find this value for your data. [▶ 🖳 See **Calculator Note 2A** to learn how to calculate the standard deviation using your calculator. ◀]

Step 4 What are the units of the statistic you calculated in Step 2? The units of the standard deviation you found in Step 3 are the same as those of the original measurements. How does your statistic compare to the standard deviation?

Step 5 If you were going to repeat the experiment, how would you change your procedures to minimize the standard deviation?

Investigation • A Good Design

With Sample Data

Name_____ Period_____ Date_____

In a well-designed experiment, you should be able to follow a specific procedure and get very similar results every time you perform the experiment. In this investigation you will consider why it's important to attempt to control the setup of an experiment in order to limit the variability of results.

Select one of these experiments.

Experiment 1: Rolling Ball

In this experiment a group of students rolled a ball of paper down a ramp and off the edge of a desk. They built the ramp from books, selecting the height and slope of the ramp and the distance from the edge of the desk. Students made a ball by crumpling a piece of paper, and rolled it down the ramp. They recorded the horizontal distance to the place where the ball hit the floor. They repeated the procedure six more times with the same ball, the same ramp setup, and the same release, and recorded their results below.

Rolling Ball Sample Data

Distance (cm)	17.3	24.4	28.7	19.2	36.8	30.8	41.6

Discovering Advanced Algebra Investigation Worksheets
©2010 Key Curriculum Press

Experiment 2: Rubber Band Launch

In this experiment students used a ruler to launch a rubber band. They selected the height and angle of the launch and the length of the stretch. They launched the rubber band into an area clear of obstructions and recorded the horizontal distance of the flight. They repeated the procedure six more times with the same rubber band, the same launch setup, and the same stretch, and recorded their results below.

Rubber Band Sample Data

Distance (cm)	182.2	135.9	187.6	162.5	150.0	186.5	180.0

Step 1   Use the data from Experiment 1 or 2. Calculate the mean distance for the trials and then calculate the deviations.

Step 2   In general, how much do the data values differ from the mean? How could the variability in the results relate to how controlled the setup was? Determine a way to calculate a *single* value that tells how accurate the group was at repeating the procedure. Write a formula to calculate your statistic using the deviations.

Step 3   A value known as the **standard deviation** helps measure the spread of data away from the mean. Use your calculator to find this value for the data. [▶ ▣ See **Calculator Note 2A** to learn how to calculate the standard deviation using your calculator. ◀]

Step 4   What are the units of the statistic you calculated in Step 2? The units of the standard deviation you found in Step 3 are the same as those of the original measurements. How does your statistic compare to the standard deviation?

Step 5   If you were going to conduct the experiment, how would you change the procedures to minimize the standard deviation?

Discovering Advanced Algebra Investigation Worksheets
©2010 Key Curriculum Press

Investigation • Eating on the Run

Name_____ Period_____ Date_____

Teenagers require anywhere from 1800 to 3200 calories per day, depending on their growth rate and level of activity. The food you consume as part of your diet should include sufficient fiber, moderate levels of carbohydrates and fat, and as little sodium, saturated fat, and cholesterol as possible. The table shows the recommended amounts of carbohydrates and fiber and the maximum amounts of other nutrients in a healthy 2500-calorie diet.

Nutrition Recommendations for a 2500-Calorie Diet

Total fat	Less than 80 g
Saturated fat	Less than 25 g
Cholesterol	Less than 300 mg
Sodium	Less than 2400 mg
Total carbohydrate	375 g
Dietary fiber	30 g

(U.S. Food and Drug Administration)

So, how does fast food fit into a healthy diet? Examine the information about the nutritional content of fast-food sandwiches. With your group, study one of the nutritional components (total calories, total fat, saturated fat, cholesterol, sodium, or total carbohydrate). Use box plots, histograms, and the measures of central tendency and spread to compare the amount of that component in the sandwiches. You may want to divide your data so that you can make comparisons between different types of sandwiches or between restaurants. As you do your statistical analysis, discuss how these fast-food items would affect a healthy diet. Prepare a short report or class presentation discussing your conclusions. [▶ 🖥 See **Calculator Note 2C** to learn how to make histograms on your calculator. ◀]

Investigation • Eating on the Run (continued)

Fast-Food Nutrition Facts

Sandwich	Total calories	Total fat (g)	Saturated fat (g)	Cholesterol (mg)	Sodium (mg)	Carbohydrate (g)
Burger King Double Whopper with Cheese	1060	69	27	185	1540	53
Carl's Jr. Western Bacon Cheeseburger	657	31	12	82	1387	65
Carl's Jr. The Six Dollar Chili Cheese Burger	926	57	27	154	1960	57
Hardee's 1/2-Lb. Grilled Sourdough Thickburger	1100	74	30	155	1430	61
Hardee's 1/2-Lb. Six Dollar Burger	1120	73	30	150	1870	72
Hardee's 1/3-Lb. Cheeseburger	680	39	19	90	1320	51
Jack in the Box Hamburger with Cheese	355	17.5	7	55	770	31
Jack in the Box Sourdough Jack	715	51	18	75	1165	36
McDonald's Quarter Pounder with Cheese	540	29	13	95	1240	39
Sonic No. 1 Sonic Burger	577	36	7	37	753	43
Wendy's Hamburger, Kids' Meal	270	9	3.5	30	610	33
Burger King Chicken Whopper	570	25	4.5	75	1410	48
Carl's Jr. Bacon Swiss Crispy Chicken Sandwich	757	38	11	91	1554	72
Carl's Jr. Carl's Western Crispy Chicken Sandwich	747	28	10	79	1875	92
Carl's Jr. Charbroiled Santa Fe Chicken Sandwich	610	32	7	97	1440	45
Carl's Jr. Southwestern Spicy Chicken Sandwich	624	41	9	63	1642	48
Dairy Queen Grilled Chicken Sandwich	340	16	2.5	55	1000	26
Jack in the Box Chicken Sandwich	390	21	4	35	730	39
Jack in the Box Chicken Sandwich with Cheese	430	24	6	45	880	40
Jack in the Box Sourdough Grilled Chicken Club	505	27	6.5	75	1220	35
McDonald's Crispy Chicken	510	26	4.5	50	1090	47
McDonald's Chicken McGrill	400	16	3	70	1020	37

(*www.foodfacts.info*)

Investigation • Match Point

Name_____ Period_____ Date_____

Below are three recursive formulas, three graphs, and three linear equations.

1. $u_0 = 4$
$u_n = u_{n-1} - 1$ where $n \geq 1$

2. $u_0 = 2$
$u_n = u_{n-1} + 5$ where $n \geq 1$

3. $u_0 = -4$
$u_n = u_{n-1} + 3$ where $n \geq 1$

A.
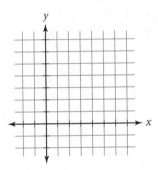

B.
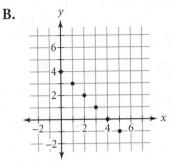

C.
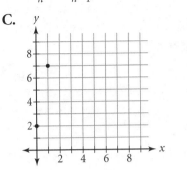

i. $y = -4 + 3x$

ii. $y = 4 + x$

iii. $y = 2 + 5x$

Step 1 Match the recursive formulas, graphs, and linear equations that go together. (Not all of the appropriate matches are listed. If the recursive rule, graph, or equation is missing, you will need to create it.) Use the space and graphs below for this.

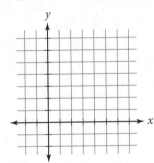
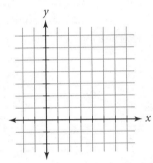

Step 2 Write a brief statement relating the starting value and common difference of an arithmetic sequence to the corresponding equation $y = a + bx$.

Step 3 Are points (n, u_n) of an arithmetic sequence always collinear? Write a brief statement supporting your answer.

Discovering Advanced Algebra Investigation Worksheets
©2010 Key Curriculum Press

Investigation • Balloon Blastoff

Name_____ Period_____ Date_____

You will need: paper, tape, a balloon, a straw, string, a motion sensor

In this investigation you will launch a rocket and use your motion sensor's data to estimate the rocket's speed. Then you will write an equation for the rocket's distance as a function of time. Choose one person to be the monitor and one person to be the launch controller.

Step 1   Hold the sensor behind the rocket. At the same time the monitor starts the sensor, the launch controller should release the balloon. Be sure nobody's hands are between the balloon and the sensor. [▶️🔲 See **Calculator Note 3C.** ◀]

Step 2   Retrieve the data from the sensor to each calculator in the group.

Step 3   Graph the data with time as the independent variable, *x*. What are the domain and range of your data? Explain.

Step 4   Sketch the graph of the data and select four representative points from the rocket data. Mark the points on your sketch and explain why you chose them.

> ### Procedure Note
>
> 1. Make a rocket of paper and tape. Design your rocket so that it can hold an inflated balloon and be taped to a drinking straw threaded on a string. Color or decorate your rocket if you like.
> 2. Tape your rocket to the straw on the string.
> 3. Inflate a balloon but do not tie off the end. The launch controller should insert it into your rocket and hold it closed.
> 4. Tie the string or hold it taut and horizontal.

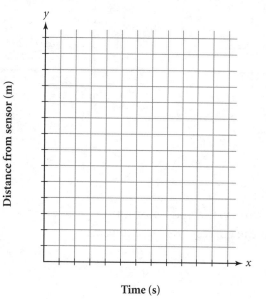

Distance from sensor (m)

Time (s)

Discovering Advanced Algebra Investigation Worksheets
©2010 Key Curriculum Press

Investigation • Balloon Blastoff (continued)

Step 5   Record the coordinates of the four points and use the points in pairs to calculate slopes. This should give six estimates of the slope.

Step 6   Are all six slope estimates that you calculated in Step 5 the same? Why or why not? Find the mean, median, and mode of your slope estimates. With your group, decide which value best represents the slope of your data. Explain why you chose this value.

Step 7   What is the real-world meaning of the slope, and how is this related to the speed of your rocket?

Name _____ Period _____ Date _____

For this investigation a group of students made a rocket, as described in the Procedure Note. They launched the rocket and used a motion sensor to gather data to estimate the rocket's speed. One student was chosen to be the monitor and another to be the launch controller. You will write an equation for the rocket's distance from the motion sensor as a function of time.

Step 1 One student held the sensor behind the rocket. At the same time the monitor started the sensor, the launch controller released the balloon.

Step 2 The students retrieved the data from the sensor to each calculator in the group. The data are recorded in this table.

Time (s)	Distance from sensor (m)
0	0.132667
0.05	0.132099
0.10	0.191364
0.15	0.276836
0.20	0.368507
0.25	0.473591
0.30	0.664749
0.35	0.94131
0.40	1.09123
0.45	1.29823
0.50	1.518573
0.55	1.744151
0.60	1.999602
0.65	2.365544
0.70	2.394023

> ## Procedure Note
> 1. Make a rocket of paper and tape. Design your rocket so that it can hold an inflated balloon and be taped to a drinking straw threaded on a string. Color or decorate your rocket if you like.
> 2. Tape your rocket to the straw on the string.
> 3. Inflate a balloon but do not tie off the end. The launch controller should insert it into your rocket and hold it closed.
> 4. Tie the string or hold it taut and horizontal.

Step 3 Graph the data with time as the independent variable, *x*. What are the domain and range of the data? Explain.

Step 4   Sketch the graph of the data and select four representative points from the rocket data. Mark the points on your sketch and explain why you chose them.

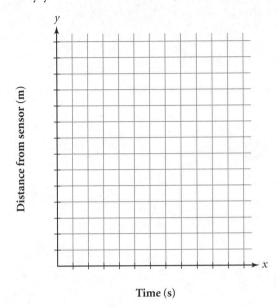

Time (s)

Step 5   Record the coordinates of the four points and use the points in pairs to calculate slopes. This should give six estimates of the slope.

Step 6   Are all six slope estimates that you calculated in Step 5 the same? Why or why not? Find the mean, median, and mode of your slope estimates. With your group, decide which value best represents the slope of the data. Explain why you chose this value.

Step 7   What is the real-world meaning of the slope, and how is this related to the speed of the rocket?

Investigation • The Wave

Name _____ **Period** _____ **Date** _____

You will need: a stopwatch or watch with a second hand

Sometimes at sporting events, people in the audience stand up quickly in succession with their arms upraised and then sit down again. The continuous rolling motion that this creates through the crowd is called "the wave." You and your class will investigate how long it takes different-size groups to do the wave.

Step 1 Using different-size groups, determine the time for each group to complete the wave. Collect at least nine pieces of data of the form (*number of people, time*), and record them in this table.

Number of people	Time (s)

Step 2   Plot the points, and find the equation of a reasonable line of fit.
Write a paragraph about your results. Be sure to answer these
questions:

- What is the slope of your line, and what is its real-world
  meaning?

- What are the *x*- and *y*-intercepts of your line, and what are their
  real-world meanings?

- What is a reasonable domain for this equation? Why?

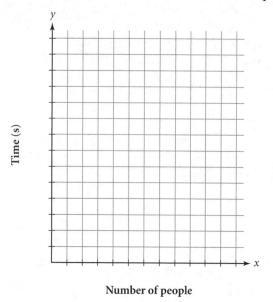

Number of people

Step 3   Can you use your line of fit to predict how long it would take
to complete the wave if everyone at your school participated?
Everyone in a large stadium? Explain why or why not.

Name_____ **Period**_____ **Date**_____

Sometimes at sporting events, people in the audience stand up quickly in succession with their arms upraised and then sit down again. The continuous rolling motion that this creates through the crowd is called "the wave." You and your class will investigate how long it takes different-size groups to do the wave.

Step 1 Using different-sized groups, a mathematics class determined the time for each group to complete the wave. They collected data of the form (*number of people, time*), and recorded them in this table.

Number of people	Time (s)
2	2.1
5	4.4
6	5.2
8	5.8
9	4.7
10	6.7
15	7.5
16	10.4
22	11.0

Step 2   Plot the points, and find the equation of a reasonable line of fit.
Write a paragraph about these results. Be sure to answer these
questions:

- What is the slope of your line, and what is its real-world
  meaning?

- What are the *x*- and *y*-intercepts of your line, and what are their
  real-world meanings?

- What is a reasonable domain for this equation? Why?

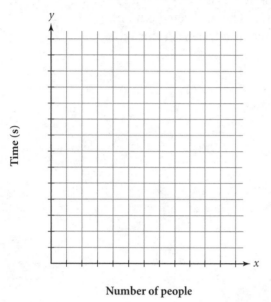

Number of people

Step 3   Can you use your line of fit to predict how long it would take to
complete the wave if everyone at the school participated? Everyone
in a large stadium? Explain why or why not.

Investigation • Airline Schedules

Name _____ **Period** _____ **Date** _____

In this investigation you will use data about airline flights to find a median-median line to model the relationship between the distance of a flight and the flight time. You will use the linear model to make predictions about flight times and distances that aren't in the table.

Destination	Flight time (min)	Distance (mi)
Cincinnati, OH	64	229
Houston, TX	189	1092
Los Angeles, CA	288	1979
Memphis, TN	104	610
Denver, CO	180	1129
Phoenix, AZ	248	1671
Louisville, KY	67	306
San Francisco, CA	303	2079
Omaha, NE	120	658
New Orleans, LA	156	938

Step 1 The flights listed here are morning departures from Detroit, Michigan. Write a complete sentence explaining what the first line of data tells you.

Step 2 Graph the data on the grid.

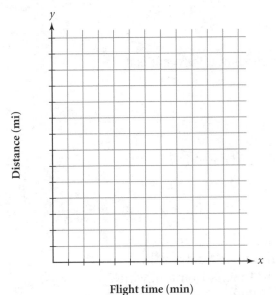

Step 3 Show the steps to calculate the median-median line through the data. Write the equation of this line. Use your calculator to check your work. [▶ 🖳 See **Calculator Note 3D** to learn how to find the median-median line with your calculator. ◀]

Step 4 On your graph, mark the three representative points used in the median-median process. Add the line to this graph.

Step 5 Answer these questions about your data and model.

  a. Use your median-median line to interpolate two points for which you did not collect data. What is the real-world meaning of each of these points?

  b. Which two points differ the most from the value predicted by your equation? Explain why.

  c. What is the real-world meaning of your slope?

  d. Find the y-intercept of your median-median line. What is its real-world meaning?

  e. What are the domain and range for your data? Why?

  f. Compare the median-median line method to the method you used in Lesson 3.3 to find the line of fit. What are the advantages and disadvantages of each? In your opinion, which method produces a better line of fit? Why?

Step 6 Summarize what you learned in this investigation and describe any difficulties you had.

Discovering Advanced Algebra Investigation Worksheets
©2010 Key Curriculum Press

Investigation • Spring Experiment

Name _____ **Period** _____ **Date** _____

You will need: a spring, a mass holder, small unit masses,
a support stand, a ruler

In this investigation you will collect data on how a spring responds to various weights. You will create a model using a median-median line and then you will use residuals to judge the accuracy of any predictions made using your model.

Step 1 Place different amounts of mass on the mass holder, recording the corresponding length of the spring each time. Collect about 10 data points of the form (*mass, spring length*). Record the data in this table.

Mass (g)	Spring length (cm)

Procedure Note

1. Attach the mass holder to the spring.
2. Hang the spring from a support, and the mass holder from the spring.
3. Measure the length of the spring (in centimeters) from the first coil to the last coil.

Investigation • Spring Experiment (continued)

Step 2 Plot the data and find the median-median line.

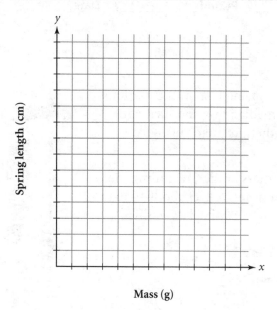

Mass (g)

Step 3 Give the real-world meanings of the slope and the *y*-intercept.

Investigation • Spring Experiment (continued)

Step 4   Use this table to organize your data and calculate the residuals. Then answer the questions.

Mass (g)	Spring length (cm)	Prediction from $\hat{y}$	Residual $(y - \hat{y})$

a. What is the sum of the residuals? Does it appear that your linear model is a good fit for the data? Explain.

b. Find the greatest positive and negative residuals. What could the magnitude of these residuals indicate?

c. If you used your model to predict the length of the spring for a particular weight and then measured the spring for that weight, would you be surprised if the predicted length and the measured length were different? Why or why not?

d. Use your model to predict the length of your spring for a weight 2 units larger than your heaviest weight. Now give an estimate in the form _?_ ± _?_ that you believe would contain the actual measured length.

Investigation • Spring Experiment

With Sample Data

Name_____ Period_____ Date_____

In this investigation you will examine data on how a spring responds to various weights. You will create a model using a median-median line and then you will use residuals to judge the accuracy of any predictions made using your model.

Step 1 A group of students set up the spring experiment by following the Procedure Note. They placed different amounts of mass on the mass holder and recorded the corresponding length of the spring each time. They collected data points of the form (*mass, spring length*) and recorded them in this table.

Mass (g)	Spring length (cm)	Prediction from $\hat{y}$	Residual $(y - \hat{y})$
50	5.0		
60	5.5		
70	6.0		
80	6.3		
90	6.8		
100	7.1		
110	7.5		
120	7.7		
130	8.1		
140	8.5		
150	8.8		
160	9.2		
170	9.5		
180	9.9		
190	10.3		
200	10.7		
210	11.3		
220	11.4		
230	11.9		
240	12.4		

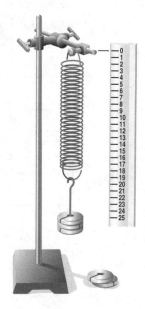

Procedure Note

1. Attach the mass holder to the spring.
2. Hang the spring from a support, and the mass holder from the spring.
3. Measure the length of the spring (in centimeters) from the first coil to the last coil.

Discovering Advanced Algebra Investigation Worksheets
©2010 Key Curriculum Press

Step 2   Plot the data and find the median-median line.

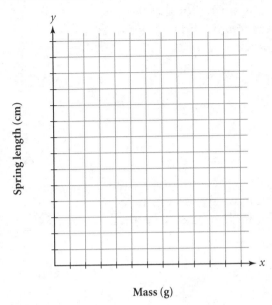

Mass (g)

Step 3   Give the real-world meanings of the slope and the *y*-intercept.

Step 4   Use the third column of the table in Step 1 to record the predicted spring lengths based on the equation for the median-median line. Then calculate the residuals and answer the questions.

   a. What is the sum of the residuals? Does it appear that your linear model is a good fit for the data? Explain.

   b. Find the greatest positive and negative residuals. What could the magnitude of these residuals indicate?

c. If you used your model to predict the length of the spring for a
particular weight and then measured the spring for that weight,
would you be surprised if the predicted length and the measured
length were different? Why or why not?

d. Use your model to predict the length of the spring for a weight
2 units larger than the heaviest weight. Now give an estimate
in the form ? ± ? that you believe would contain the actual
measured length.

Discovering Advanced Algebra Investigation Worksheets
©2010 Key Curriculum Press

Investigation • Population Trends

Name _____ Period _____ Date _____

The table below gives the populations of San Jose, California, and Detroit, Michigan.

Populations

Year	1950	1960	1970	1980	1990	2000	2005
San Jose	95,280	204,196	459,913	629,400	782,248	894,943	912,232
Detroit	1,849,568	1,670,144	1,514,063	1,203,368	1,027,974	951,270	886,671

(*The World Almanac and Book of Facts 2007*)

Step 1   Estimate the year that the two cities had the same population. What was that population?

Step 2   Show the method you used to make this prediction. Choose a different method to check your answer. Discuss the pros and cons of each method.

Investigation • What's Your System?

Name_____ Period_____ Date_____

In this investigation you will discover different classifications of systems and their properties. You can divide up the work among group members, but make sure each problem is solved by one person and checked by another.

Step 1   Use the method of elimination to solve each system. (Don't be surprised if it doesn't always work.)

a. $\begin{cases} 2x + 5y = 6 \\ 2x - 3y = 22 \end{cases}$ b. $\begin{cases} 3x + 2y = 12 \\ -6x - 4y = -24 \end{cases}$ c. $\begin{cases} 4x - 8y = 5 \\ -3x + 6y = 11 \end{cases}$

d. $\begin{cases} -2x + y = 5 \\ 6x - 3y = -15 \end{cases}$ e. $\begin{cases} x + 3y = 6 \\ 5x - 3y = 6 \end{cases}$ f. $\begin{cases} x + 3y = 8 \\ 3x + 9y = -4 \end{cases}$

Step 2   Graph each system in Step 1.

a.

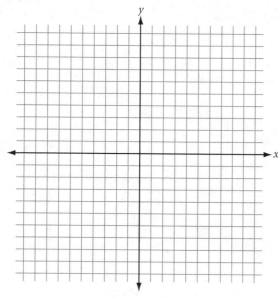

b.

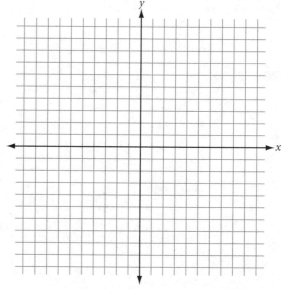

Discovering Advanced Algebra Investigation Worksheets
©2010 Key Curriculum Press

c.

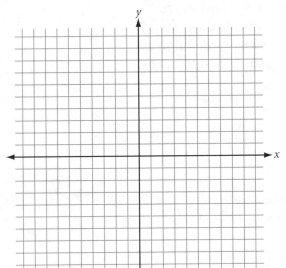

d.

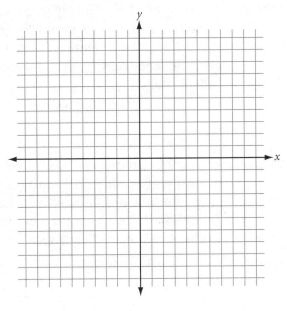

e.

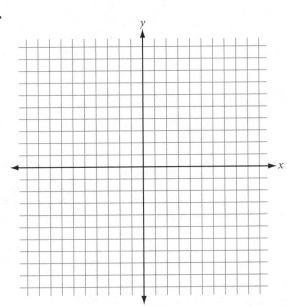

f.

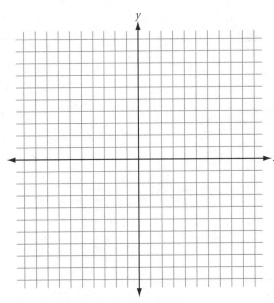

Step 3 A system that has a solution (a point or points of intersection) is called **consistent.** Which of the six systems in Step 1 are consistent?

Step 4 A system that has no solution (no point of intersection) is called **inconsistent.** Which of the systems in Step 1 are inconsistent?

Step 5   A system that has infinitely many solutions is called **dependent.**
For linear systems, this means the equations are equivalent (though
they may not look identical). A system that has a single solution is
called **independent.** Which of the systems in Step 1 are dependent?
Independent?

Step 6   Your graphs from Step 2 helped you classify each system as
inconsistent or consistent and as dependent or independent.
Now look at your solutions from Step 1. Make a conjecture
about how the results of the elimination method can be used
to classify a system of equations.

Investigation • Graph a Story

Name_____ Period_____ Date_____

Every graph tells a story. Make a graph to go with the story in Part 1. Then invent your own story to go with the graph in Part 2.

Part 1

Sketch a graph that reflects all the information given in this story.

"It was a dark and stormy night. Before the torrents of rain came, the bucket was empty. The rain subsided at daybreak. The bucket remained untouched through the morning until Old Dog Trey arrived as thirsty as a dog. The sun shone brightly through the afternoon. Then Billy, the kid next door, arrived. He noticed two plugs in the side of the bucket. One of them was about a quarter of the way up, and the second one was near the bottom. As fast as you could blink an eye, he pulled out the plugs and ran away."

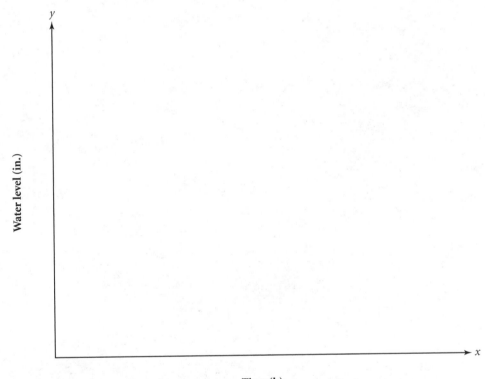

Part 2

This graph tells a story. It could be a story about a lake, a bathtub, or whatever you imagine. Spend some time with your group discussing the information contained in the graph. Write a story that conveys all of this information, including when and how the rates of change increase or decrease.

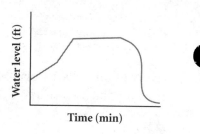

Discovering Advanced Algebra Investigation Worksheets
©2010 Key Curriculum Press

Investigation • To Be or Not to Be (a Function)

Name_____ Period_____ Date_____

Below are nine representations of relations.

a.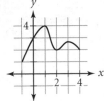

b.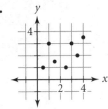

c.

d.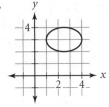

e.

f.

g. independent variable: the age of each student in your class
   dependent variable: the height of each student

h. independent variable: an automobile in the state of Kentucky
   dependent variable: that automobile's license plate number

i. independent variable: the day of the year
   dependent variable: the time of sunset

Step 1 Identify each relation that is also a function. For each relation that is not a function, explain why not.

a.

b.

c.

d.

e.

f.

g.

h.

i.

Step 2   For each graph or table that represents a function in parts a–f, find the y-value when $x = 2$, and find the x-value(s) when $y = 3$. Write each answer in function notation using the letter of the subpart as the function name. For example, if graph a represents a function, $a(2) = \underline{\ ?\ }$ and $a(\underline{\ ?\ }) = 3$.

Investigation • Movin' Around

Name_____   **Period**_____   **Date**_____

You will need: two motion sensors

In this investigation you will explore what happens to the equation of a linear function when you translate the graph of the line. You'll then use your discoveries to interpret data. Graph the lines in Steps 1–4 on the given set of axes and look for patterns.

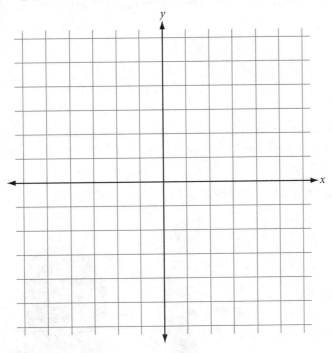

Step 1   Graph the line $y = 2x$ and then draw a line parallel to it, but 3 units higher. What is the equation of this new line? If $f(x) = 2x$, what is the equation of the new line in terms of $f(x)$?

Step 2   Draw a line parallel to the line $y = 2x$, but shifted down 4 units. What is the equation of this line? If $f(x) = 2x$, what is the equation of the new line in terms of $f(x)$?

Step 3   Mark the point where the line $y = 2x$ passes through the origin. Plot a point right 3 units from the origin. Draw a line parallel to the original line through this point. Use the point to write an equation in point-slope form for the new line. Then write an equation for the line in terms of $f(x)$.

Investigation • Movin' Around (continued)

Step 4   Plot a point left 1 unit and up 2 units from the origin. Draw a line parallel to the original line through this point and use the point to write an equation in point-slope form for the new line. Then write an equation for the line in terms of $f(x)$.

Step 5   If you move every point on the function $y = f(x)$ to a new point up k units and right h units, what is the equation of this translated function?

Your group will now use motion sensors to create a function and a translated copy of that function. [▸ 🖳 See **Calculator Note 4C** for instructions on how to collect and retrieve data from two motion sensors. ◂]

Step 6   Arrange your group as in the photo to collect data.

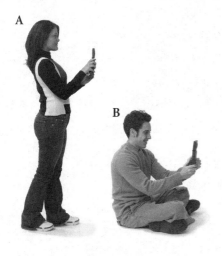

Step 7   Person D coordinates the collection of data like this:

At 0 seconds:	C begins to walk slowly toward the motion sensors, and A begins to collect data.
About 2 seconds:	B begins to collect data.
About 5 seconds:	C begins to walk backward.
About 10 seconds:	A's sensor stops.
About 12 seconds:	B's sensor stops and C stops walking.

Step 8 After collecting the data, follow Calculator Note 4C to retrieve the data to two calculators and then transmit four lists of data to each group member's calculator. Be sure to keep track of which data each list contains.

Step 9 Graph both sets of data on the same screen. Record a sketch of what you see and answer these questions:

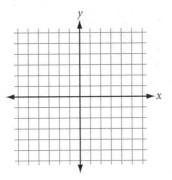

   a. How are the two graphs related to each other?

   b. If A's graph is $y = f(x)$, what equation describes B's graph? Describe how you determined this equation.

   c. In general, if the graph of $y = f(x)$ is translated horizontally h units and vertically k units, what is the equation of this translated function?

Name_____   Period_____   Date_____

In this investigation you will explore what happens to the equation of a linear function when you translate the graph of the line. Graph the lines in Steps 1–4 on the given set of axes and look for patterns.

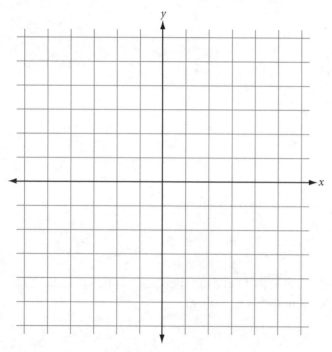

Step 1   On the grid, graph the line $y = 2x$ and then draw a line parallel to it, but 3 units higher. What is the equation of this new line? If $f(x) = 2x$, what is the equation of the new line in terms of $f(x)$?

Step 2   Draw a line parallel to the line $y = 2x$, but shifted down 4 units. What is the equation of this line? If $f(x) = 2x$, what is the equation of the new line in terms of $f(x)$?

Step 3   Mark the point where the line $y = 2x$ passes through the origin. Plot a point right 3 units from the origin. Draw a line parallel to the original line through this point. Use the point to write an equation in point-slope form for the new line. Then write an equation for the line in terms of $f(x)$.

Discovering Advanced Algebra Investigation Worksheets
©2010 Key Curriculum Press

Step 4   Plot a point left 1 unit and up 2 units from the origin. Draw a line parallel to the original line through this point and use the point to write an equation in point-slope form for the new line. Then write an equation for the line in terms of $f(x)$.

Step 5   If you move every point on the function $y = f(x)$ to a new point up k units and right h units, what is the equation of this translated function?

Investigation • Make My Graph

Name_____ **Period**_____ **Date**_____

Step 1 Each graph below shows the graph of the parent function $y = x^2$ with vertex at $(0, 0)$. Find a quadratic equation that produces the congruent parabola graph with plotted points. Apply what you learned about translations of the graphs of functions in Lesson 4.3.

> **Procedure Note**
>
> Different calculators have different resolutions. A good graphing window will help you make use of the resolution to better identify points.
> [▶ ▦ See **Calculator Note 4D** to find a good window setting for your calculator. ◀]
> Enter the parent function $y = x^2$ as the first equation. Enter the equation for the transformation as the second equation. Graph both equations to check your work.

a.
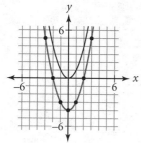

b.
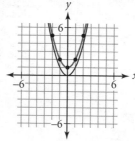

c.
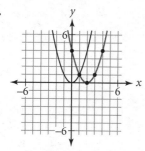

d.
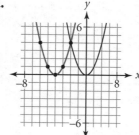

e.
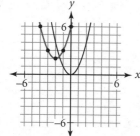

f.
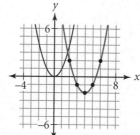

Discovering Advanced Algebra Investigation Worksheets
©2010 Key Curriculum Press

Investigation • Make My Graph (continued)

Step 2   Write a few sentences describing any connections you discovered between the graphs of the translated parabolas, the equation for the translated parabola, and the equation of the parent function $y = x^2$.

Step 3   In general, what is the equation of the parabola formed when the graph of $y = x^2$ is translated horizontally h units and vertically k units?

Investigation • Take a Moment to Reflect

Name _____ **Period** _____ **Date** _____

In this investigation you first will work with linear functions to discover how to create a new transformation—a **reflection.** Then you will apply reflections to quadratic functions and square root functions. Sketch your graphs on the grids.

Step 1   Graph $f_1(x) = 0.5x + 2$ on your calculator.

     a. Make a sketch to predict what the graph of $-f_1(x)$ will look like. Then check your prediction by graphing $f_2(x) = -f_1(x)$.

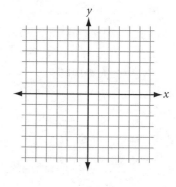

     b. Change f_1 to $f_1(x) = -2x - 4$, and repeat the instructions in Step 1a.

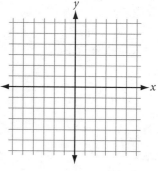

     c. Change f_1 to $f_1(x) = x^2 + 1$ and repeat.

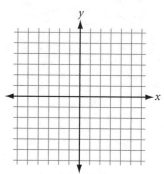

     d. In general, how are the graphs of $y = f(x)$ and $y = -f(x)$ related?

Discovering Advanced Algebra Investigation Worksheets
©2010 Key Curriculum Press

Step 2   Graph $f_1(x) = 0.5x + 2$ on your calculator.

    a. Make a sketch to predict what the graph of $f_1(-x)$ will look like. Then check your prediction by graphing $f_2(x) = f_1(-x)$.

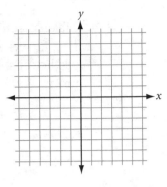

    b. Change f_1 to $f_1(x) = -2x - 4$, and repeat the instructions in Step 2a.

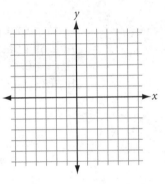

    c. Change f_1 to $f_1(x) = x^2 + 1$ and repeat. Explain what happens.

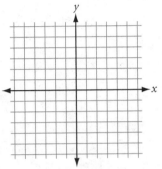

    d. Change f_1 to $f_1(x) = (x - 3)^2 + 2$ and repeat.

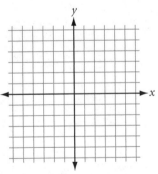

    e. In general, how are the graphs of $y = f(x)$ and $y = f(-x)$ related?

Step 3 Graph $f_1(x) = \sqrt{x}$ on your calculator.

a. Make a sketch to predict what the graphs of $f_2 = -f_1(x)$ and $f_3 = f_1(-x)$ will look like. Use your calculator to verify your predictions. Write equations for both of these functions in terms of x.

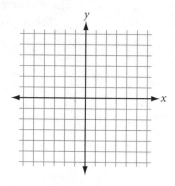

b. Make a sketch to predict what the graph of $f_4 = -f_1(-x)$ will look like. Use your calculator to verify your prediction.

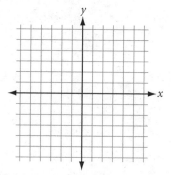

c. Notice that the graph of the square root function looks like half of a parabola, oriented horizontally. Why isn't it an entire parabola? What function would you graph to complete the bottom half of the parabola?

Discovering Advanced Algebra Investigation Worksheets
©2010 Key Curriculum Press

Investigation • The Pendulum

Name _____   **Period** _____   **Date** _____

You will need: string, a small weight, a stopwatch or a watch with
a second hand

Italian mathematician and astronomer Galileo Galilei (1564–1642) made
many contributions to our understanding of gravity, the physics of falling
objects, and the orbits of the planets. One of his famous experiments
involved the periodic motion of a pendulum. In this investigation you will
carry out the same experiment and find a function to model the data.

Step 1   Follow the Procedure Note to find the period of your
pendulum. Repeat the experiment for several different string
lengths and complete the table of values. Use a variety of
short, medium, and long string lengths.

Length (cm)	Period (s)

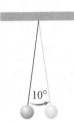

Procedure Note

1. Tie a weight at one end of
   a length of string to make a
   pendulum. Firmly hold the
   other end of the string, or tie
   it to something, so that the
   weight hangs freely.
2. Measure the length of the
   pendulum, from the center
   of the weight to the point
   where the string is held.
3. Pull the weight to one side
   and release it so that it
   swings back and forth in a
   short arc, about 10° to 20°.
   Time ten complete swings
   (forward and back is one
   swing).
4. The **period** of your pendulum
   is the time for one complete
   swing (forward and back).
   Find the period by dividing
   by 10.

Investigation • The Pendulum (continued)

Step 2   Graph the data using *length* as the independent variable. What is the shape of the graph? What do you suppose is the parent function?

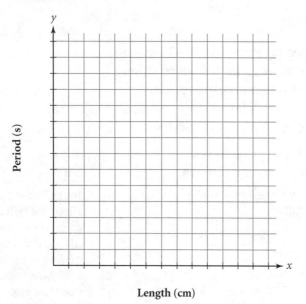

Length (cm)

Step 3   The vertex is at the origin, $(0, 0)$. Why do you suppose it is there?

Step 4   Have each member of your group choose a different data point and use that data point to find the horizontal and vertical dilations. Apply these transformations to find an equation to fit the data.

Step 5   Compare the collection of equations from your group. Which points are the best to use to fit the curve? Why do these points work better than others?

Discovering Advanced Algebra Investigation Worksheets
©2010 Key Curriculum Press

Investigation • The Pendulum

With Sample Data

Name _____ Period _____ Date _____

Italian mathematician and astronomer Galileo Galilei (1564–1642) made many contributions to our understanding of gravity, the physics of falling objects, and the orbits of the planets. One of his famous experiments involved the periodic motion of a pendulum. In this investigation you will review data from the same experiment and find a function to model the data.

Step 1 A group of students followed the Procedure Note to find the period of a pendulum. They repeated the experiment using a variety of short, medium, and long string lengths and completed this table of values.

Length (cm)	Period (s)
100	2.0
85	1.9
75	1.8
30	1.4
15	0.9
5	0.6
43	1.4
60	1.6
89	2.0
140	2.4
180	2.6
195	2.9

Procedure Note

1. Tie a weight at one end of a length of string to make a pendulum. Firmly hold the other end of the string, or tie it to something, so that the weight hangs freely.
2. Measure the length of the pendulum, from the center of the weight to the point where the string is held.
3. Pull the weight to one side and release it so that it swings back and forth in a short arc, about 10° to 20°. Time ten complete swings (forward and back is one swing).
4. The **period** of your pendulum is the time for one complete swing (forward and back). Find the period by dividing by 10.

Step 2   Graph the data using *length* as the independent variable. What
is the shape of the graph? What do you suppose is the parent
function?

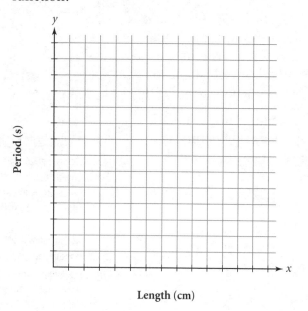

Length (cm)

Step 3   The vertex is at the origin, $(0, 0)$. Why do you suppose it is there?

Step 4   Have each member of your group choose a different data point
and use that data point to find the horizontal and vertical dilations.
Apply these transformations to find an equation to fit the data.

Step 5   Compare the collection of equations from your group. Which
points are the best to use to fit the curve? Why do these points
work better than others?

Discovering Advanced Algebra Investigation Worksheets
©2010 Key Curriculum Press

Investigation • When Is a Circle Not a Circle?

Name _____ **Period** _____ **Date** _____

You will need: ruler, Coordinate Axes worksheet (optional)

If you look at a circle, like the top rim of a cup, from an angle, you don't see
a circle; you see an ellipse. Choose one of the ellipses shown below. Use your
ruler carefully to place axes on the ellipse, and scale your axes in centimeters.
Be sure to place the axes so that the longest dimension is parallel to one of the
axes. Find the equation to model your ellipse. Graph your equation on your
calculator and verify that it creates an ellipse with the same dimensions as on
this Investigation Worksheet.

Investigation • Looking Up

Name _____   Period _____   Date _____

You will need: a small mirror, one or more tape measures or
metersticks

First, you'll establish a relationship between your distance from a mirror and
what you can see in it.

Step 1   Set up the experiment as in the Procedure Note. Stand a
short distance from the mirror, and look down into it. Move
slightly left or right until you can see the tape measure on the
wall reflected in the mirror.

Step 2   Have a group member slide his or her finger up the wall to
help locate the highest height mark that is reflected in the
mirror. In the table record the height in centimeters, h, and
the distance from your toe to the center of the mirror in
centimeters, d.

Distance d (cm)	Height h (cm)

Step 3   Change your distance from the mirror and repeat
Step 2. Make sure you keep your head in the same
position. Collect several pairs of data in the form (d, h).
Include some distances from the mirror that are small
and some that are large.

Step 4   Find a function that fits your data by transforming
the parent function $h = \frac{1}{d}$. Call this function f.

Now you'll combine your work from Steps 1–4 with the scenario of a timed
walk toward and away from the mirror.

Discovering Advanced Algebra Investigation Worksheets
©2010 Key Curriculum Press

Investigation • Looking Up (continued)

Step 5 Suppose this table gives your position at 1-second intervals:

Time (s) t	0	1	2	3	4	5	6	7
Distance to mirror (cm) d	163	112	74	47	33	31	40	62

Use one of the families of functions from this chapter to fit these data. Call this function g. It should give the distance from the mirror for seconds 0 to 7.

Step 6 Use your two functions to answer these questions:

a. How high up the wall can you see when you are 47 cm from the mirror?

b. Where are you at 1.3 seconds?

c. How high up the wall can you see at 3.4 seconds?

Step 7 Change each expression into words relating to the context of this investigation and find an answer. Show the steps you needed to evaluate each expression.

a. $f(60)$

b. $g(5.1)$

c. $f(g(2.8))$

Step 8 Find a single function, $H(t)$, that does the work of $f(g(t))$. Show that $H(2.8)$ gives the same answer as Step 7c above.

Name_____ **Period**_____ **Date**_____

First, you'll establish a relationship between your distance from a mirror and what you can see in it.

Step 1   Students set up an experiment as in the Procedure Note. One person stood a short distance from the mirror and looked down into it. He moved until he could see the tape measure on the wall reflected in the mirror.

Step 2   Another person slid his finger up the wall to help locate the highest height mark that was reflected in the mirror. The group made this table and recorded the height in centimeters, h, and the distance from the first person's toe to the center of the mirror in centimeters, d.

> **Procedure Note**
> 1. Place the mirror flat on the floor 0.5 m from a wall.
> 2. Use tape to attach tape measures or metersticks up the wall to a height of 1.5 to 2 m.

Distance d (cm)	Height h (cm)
50	148
70	106
100	73.5
130	57
160	45

Step 3   The first person changed his distance from the mirror, keeping his head in the same position, and the group repeated Step 2. They added more pairs of data to the table, in the form, (d, h), including some distances from the mirror that were small and some that were large.

Step 4   Find a function that fits the data by transforming the parent function $h = \frac{1}{d}$. Call this function f.

Now you'll combine the work from Steps 1–4 with the scenario of a timed walk toward and away from the mirror.

Discovering Advanced Algebra Investigation Worksheets
©2010 Key Curriculum Press

Step 5   Suppose this table gives the student's position at 1-second intervals:

Time (s) t	0	1	2	3	4	5	6	7
Distance to mirror (cm) d	163	112	74	47	33	31	40	62

Use one of the families of functions from this chapter to fit these data. Call this function g. It should give the distance from the mirror for seconds 0 to 7.

Step 6   Use your two functions to answer these questions:

   a. How high up the wall could you see if you are 47 cm from the mirror?

   b. Where would you be at 1.3 seconds?

   c. How high up the wall could you see at 3.4 seconds?

Step 7   Change each expression into words relating to the context of this investigation and find an answer. Show the steps you needed to evaluate each expression.

   a. $f(60)$

   b. $g(5.1)$

   c. $f(g(2.8))$

Step 8   Find a single function, $H(t)$, that does the work of $f(g(t))$. Show that $H(2.8)$ gives the same answer as Step 7c above.

Investigation • Radioactive Decay

Name _____ **Period** _____ **Date** _____

You will need: one die per person

This investigation is a simulation of radioactive decay. Each person will need a standard six-sided die. [▶ 🖥 See **Calculator Note 1L** to simulate this with your calculator instead. ◀] Each standing person represents a radioactive atom in a sample. The people who sit down at each stage represent the atoms that underwent radioactive decay.

Step 1   Follow the Procedure Note to collect data in the form (*stage, number standing*). Record the data in the table.

Stage	Number of people standing

> ### Procedure Note
>
> 1. All members of the class should stand up, except for the recorder. The recorder counts and records the number standing at each stage.
> 2. Each standing person rolls a die, and anyone who gets a 1 sits down.
> 3. Wait for the recorder to count and record the number of people standing.
> 4. Repeat Steps 2 and 3 until fewer than three students are standing.

Investigation • Radioactive Decay (continued)

Step 2   Graph your data on the grid. The graph should remind you of the
sequence graphs you studied in Chapter 1. What type of sequence
does this resemble?

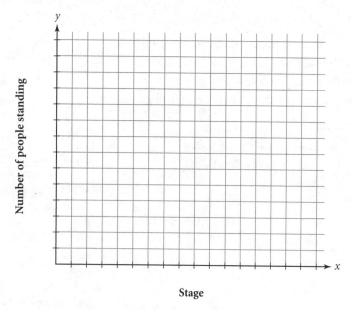

Stage

Step 3   Identify u_0 and the common ratio, r, for your sequence. Complete
the table below. Use the values of u_0 and r to help you write
an explicit formula for your data.

n	u_n	u_n in terms of u_0 and r	u_n in terms of u_0 and r using exponents
0	u_0	/////////	
1	u_1	$u_0 \cdot r$	
2	u_2	$u_0 \cdot r \cdot r$	
3	u_3	$u_0 \cdot r \cdot r \cdot r$	
...	...	...	...
n	u_n	/////////	

Discovering Advanced Algebra Investigation Worksheets
©2010 Key Curriculum Press

Investigation • Radioactive Decay (continued)

Step 4   Graph your explicit formula along with your data. Notice where
the value of u_0 appears in your equation. Your graph should pass
through the original data point $(0, u_0)$. Modify your equation so
that it passes through $(1, u_1)$, the second data point. (Think about
translating the graph horizontally and also changing the starting
value.)

Step 5   Experiment with changing your equation to pass through other
data points. Decide on an equation that you think is the best fit
for your data. Write a sentence or two explaining why you chose
this equation.

Step 6   What equation with ratio r would you write that contains the
point $(6, u_6)$?

This investigation is a simulation of radioactive decay. Each standing person represents a radioactive atom in a sample. The people who sit down at each stage represent the atoms that underwent radioactive decay.

Step 1   The students in a mathematics class followed the Procedure Note to collect data in the form (*stage, number standing*). They recorded those data in this table.

Stage	Number of people standing
0	30
1	26
2	19
3	17
4	14
5	12
6	11
7	9
8	8
9	8
10	5
11	5
12	2

Procedure Note

1. All members of the class should stand up, except for the recorder. The recorder counts and records the number standing at each stage.
2. Each standing person rolls a die, and anyone who gets a 1 sits down.
3. Wait for the recorder to count and record the number of people standing.
4. Repeat Steps 2 and 3 until fewer than three students are standing.

Step 2   Graph the data on the grid. The graph should remind you of the
sequence graphs you studied in Chapter 1. What type of sequence
does this resemble?

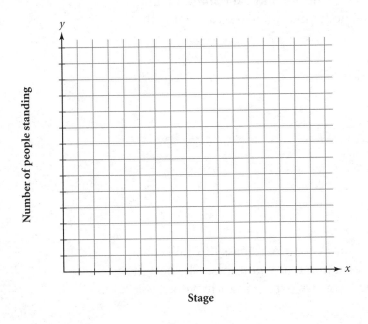

Step 3   Identify u_0 and the common ratio, r, for the sequence. Complete
the table below. Use the values of u_0 and r to help you write
an explicit formula for the data.

n	u_n	u_n in terms of u_0 and r	u_n in terms of u_0 and r using exponents
0	u_0	/////////	
1	u_1	$u_0 \cdot r$	
2	u_2	$u_0 \cdot r \cdot r$	
3	u_3	$u_0 \cdot r \cdot r \cdot r$	
...	...	...	...
n	u_n	/////////	

Step 4 Graph your explicit formula along with the data. Notice where
the value of u_0 appears in your equation. Your graph should pass
through the original data point $(0, u_0)$. Modify your equation
so that it passes through $(1, u_1)$, the second data point. (Think
about translating the graph horizontally and also changing the
starting value.)

Step 5 Experiment with changing your equation to pass through other
data points. Decide on an equation that you think is the best fit
for the data. Write a sentence or two explaining why you chose
this equation.

Step 6 What equation with ratio r would you write that contains the
point $(6, u_6)$?

Discovering Advanced Algebra Investigation Worksheets
©2010 Key Curriculum Press

Investigation • Properties of Exponents

Name_____ Period_____ Date_____

Use expanded form to review and generalize the properties of exponents.

Step 1   Write each product in expanded form, and then rewrite it in exponential form.

   a. $2^3 \cdot 2^4$ **b.** $x^5 \cdot x^{12}$ **c.** $10^2 \cdot 10^5$

Step 2   Generalize your results from Step 1. $a^m \cdot a^n = $ _____

Step 3   Write the numerator and denominator of each quotient in expanded form. Reduce by eliminating common factors, and then rewrite the factors that remain in exponential form.

   a. $\dfrac{4^5}{4^2}$ **b.** $\dfrac{x^8}{x^6}$ **c.** $\dfrac{(0.94)^{15}}{(0.94)^5}$

Step 4   Generalize your results from Step 3. $\dfrac{a^m}{a^n} = $ _____

Step 5   Write each quotient in expanded form, reduce, and rewrite in exponential form.

   a. $\dfrac{2^3}{2^4}$ **b.** $\dfrac{4^5}{4^7}$ **c.** $\dfrac{x^3}{x^8}$

Step 6   Rewrite each quotient in Step 5 using the property you discovered in Step 4.

Step 7   Generalize your results from Steps 5 and 6. $\dfrac{1}{a^n} = $ _____

Step 8 Write several expressions in the form $(a^n)^m$. Expand each expression, and then rewrite it in exponential form. Generalize your results.

Step 9 Write several expressions in the form $(a \cdot b)^n$. Don't multiply a times b. Expand each expression, and then rewrite it in exponential form. Generalize your results.

Step 10 Show that $a^0 = 1$, using the properties you have discovered. Write at least two exponential expressions to support your explanation.

Investigation • Getting to the Root

Name _____ **Period** _____ **Date** _____

In this investigation you'll explore the relationship between x and $x^{1/2}$ and learn how to find the values of some expressions with rational exponents.

Step 1 Use your calculator to create a table for $y = x^{1/2}$ at integer values of x. Record the data in this table. When is $x^{1/2}$ a positive integer? Describe the relationship between x and $x^{1/2}$.

x	$y = x^{1/2}$

Step 2 Graph $y = x^{1/2}$ in a graphing window with x- and y-values less than 10. Sketch your graph on this grid. This graph should look familiar to you. Make a conjecture about what other function is equivalent to $y = x^{1/2}$, enter your guess as a second equation, and verify that the equations give the same y-value at each x-value.

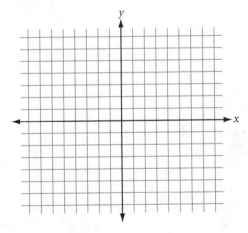

Step 3 State what you have discovered about raising a number to a power of $\frac{1}{2}$. Include an example with your statement.

Step 4   Clear the previous functions, and make a table for $y = 25^x$ with x
           incrementing by $\frac{1}{2}$. Record the data in this table.

x	y = 25ˣ

Step 5   Study your table and explain any relationships you see. How could
           you find the value of $49^{3/2}$ without a calculator? Check your answer
           using a calculator.

Step 6   How could you find the value of $27^{2/3}$ without a calculator? Verify
           your response and then test your strategy on $8^{5/3}$. Check your
           answer.

Step 7   Describe what it means to raise a number to a rational exponent,
           and generalize a procedure for simplifying $a^{m/n}$.

Discovering Advanced Algebra Investigation Worksheets
©2010 Key Curriculum Press

Investigation • The Inverse

Name_____ Period_____ Date_____

In this investigation you will use graphs, tables, and equations to explore the inverses of several functions.

Step 1   Graph the equation $f(x) = 6 + 3x$ on your calculator. Complete the table for this function.

x	−1	0	1	2	3
y					

Step 2   Because the inverse is obtained by switching the independent and dependent variables, you can find five points on the inverse of function f by swapping the x- and y-coordinates in the table. Complete the table for the inverse.

x					
y	−1	0	1	2	3

Step 3   Graph the five points you found in Step 2 by creating a scatter plot. Describe the graph and write an equation for it. Graph your equation and verify that it passes through the points in the table from Step 2.

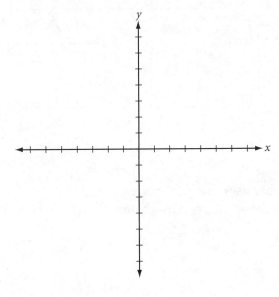

Investigation • The Inverse (continued)

Step 4 Repeat Steps 1–3 for each of these functions. You may need to write more than one equation to describe the inverse.

i. $g(x) = \sqrt{x+1} - 3$

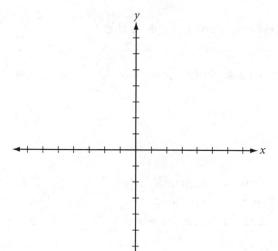

Step 1 Table

x					
y					

Step 2 Table

x				
y				

ii. $h(x) = (x-2)^2 - 5$

Step 1 Table

x				
y				

Step 2 Table

x				
y				

Step 5 Study the graphs of functions and their inverses that you made. What observations can you make about the graphs of a function and its inverse?

Step 6 You create the inverse by switching the *x*- and *y*-values of the points. How can you apply this idea to find the equation of the inverse from the original function? Verify that your method works by using it to find the equations for the inverses of functions *f*, *g*, and *h*.

Discovering Advanced Algebra Investigation Worksheets
©2010 Key Curriculum Press

Investigation • Exponents and Logarithms

Name_____ **Period**_____ **Date**_____

In this investigation you'll discover the connection between exponents on the base 10 and logarithms.

Step 1 Graph the function $f(x) = 10^x$ for $-1.5 \leq x \leq 1.5$ on your calculator. Sketch the graph and complete the table of information.

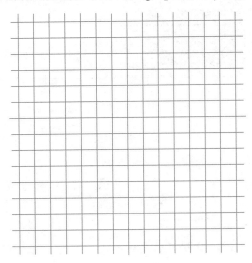

Domain	
Range	
x-intercept	
y-intercept	
Equation of asymptote	

Step 2 Complete the table of values for $f(x) = 10^x$ and its inverse.

x	−1.5	−1	−0.5	0	0.5	1	1.5
f(x)							

x							
$f^{-1}(x)$	−1.5	−1	−0.5	0	0.5	1	1.5

Step 3   Enter the points for the inverse of $f(x)$ into your calculator and
plot them. You will need to adjust the graphing window in order
to see these points. Sketch the graph of the inverse function, and
complete the table of information about the inverse.

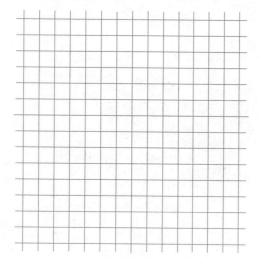

Domain	
Range	
x-intercept	
y-intercept	
Equation of asymptote	

Step 4   This inverse function is called the logarithm of x, or $\log(x)$. Enter
the equation $y = \log(x)$ into your calculator. Trace your graphs or
use tables to find the following values. [▶▢ See **Calculator Note 5C** to find
out how to work with logarithms on your calculator. ◀]

a. $10^{1.5}$ b. $\log(10^{1.5})$ c. $\log 0.32$ d. $10^{\log 0.32}$

e. $10^{1.2}$ f. $\log(10^{1.2})$ g. $10^{\log 25}$ h. $\log 10^{2.8}$

Step 5   Based on your results from Step 4, what is $\log 10^x$? Explain.

Step 6   Based on your results from Step 4, what is $10^{\log x}$? Explain.

Investigation • Exponents and Logarithms (continued)

Step 7 Using your results from Steps 4–6, complete the following statements:

    a. If $100 = 10^2$, then $\log 100 =$ _____ .

    b. If $400 \approx 10^{2.6021}$, then $\log$ _____ $\approx$ _____ .

    c. If _____ ≈ 10 ——— , then $\log 500 \approx$ _____ .

Step 8 Complete the following statement:

    If $y = 10^x$, then $\log$ _____ $=$ _____ .

Investigation • Properties of Logarithms

Name_____ Period_____ Date_____

Step 1   Use your calculator to complete the table. Record the values to three decimal places.

Step 2   Look closely at the values for the logarithms in the table. Look for pairs of values that add up to a third value in the table. For example, add log 2 and log 3. Where can you find that sum in the table?

Record the equations that you find in the form log 2 + log 3 = log _?_ . (*Hint:* You should find at least six equations.)

Log form	Decimal form
Log 2	0.301
Log 3	
Log 5	
Log 6	
Log 8	
Log 9	
Log 10	
Log 12	
Log 15	
Log 16	
Log 25	
Log 27	

Step 3   Write a conjecture based on your results from Step 2.

Step 4   Use your conjecture to write log 90 as the sum of two logs. Do the same for log 30 and log 72. Then use the table and your calculator to test your conjecture.

Complete the following statement:

$\log a + \log b = \log$ _____ .

Discovering Advanced Algebra Investigation Worksheets
©2010 Key Curriculum Press

Step 5   Now find pairs of values in the table that subtract to equal another value in the table. Record your results in the form $\log 9 - \log 3 = \log$ _____. Describe any patterns you see.

Complete the following statement:

$$\log a - \log b = \log \text{_____}.$$

Step 6   Now find values in the table that can be multiplied by a small integer to give another value in the table, such as $3 \cdot \log 2 =$ _____. Describe any patterns you see. You may want to think about different ways to express numbers such as 25 or 27 using exponents.

Complete the following statement: $b \cdot \log a = \log$ _____.

Step 7   How do the properties you recorded in Steps 4–6 relate to the properties of exponents?

Investigation • Cooling

Name _____ **Period** _____ **Date** _____

You will need: a cup of hot water (optional), a temperature probe, a data-collection device (optional), a second temperature probe (optional)

In this investigation you will find a relationship between temperature of a cooling object and time.

Step 1 Connect a temperature probe to your calculator or a data collector and set it up to collect 18 data points over 180 seconds, or 1 data point every 10 seconds. Heat the end of the probe by placing it in hot water or holding it tightly in the palm of your hand. When it is hot, set the probe on a table so that the tip is not touching anything and begin data collection. [▶🖳 See **Calculator Note 5D.** ◀] Record the data in the first two columns of the table.

Time (s) t	Temperature (°C) p	$p - L$	$\log(p - L)$

Discovering Advanced Algebra Investigation Worksheets
©2010 Key Curriculum Press

Investigation • Cooling (continued)

Step 2   Let t be the time in seconds, and let p be the temperature of the probe. While you are collecting the data, draw a sketch of what you expect the graph of (t, p) data to look like as the temperature probe cools. Label the axes and mark the scale on your graph. Did everyone in your group draw the same graph? Discuss any differences of opinion.

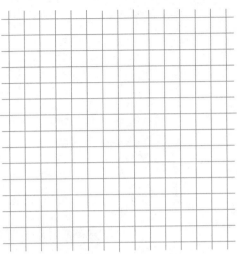

Step 3   Plot the data in the form (t, p) on an appropriately scaled graph. Your graph should appear to be an exponential function. Study the graph and the data, and guess the temperature limit, L. You could also use a second temperature probe to measure the room temperature, L.

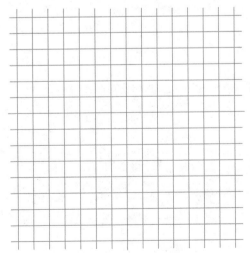

Investigation • Cooling (continued)

Step 4   Subtract this limit from your temperatures, and record the data in the third column in the table. Find the logarithm of the new data, and complete the last column in the table. Plot data in the form $(t, \log(p - L))$. If the data are not linear, then try a different limit.

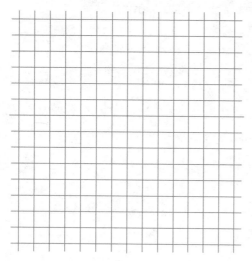

Step 5   Find the equation that models the data in Step 4, and use this to find an equation that models the (t, p) data in Step 3. Give the real-world meanings of the values in the final equation.

Discovering Advanced Algebra Investigation Worksheets
©2010 Key Curriculum Press

Name _____ Period _____ Date _____

In this investigation you will find a relationship between temperature of a cooling object and time.

Step 1 To carry out this investigation, a group of students connected a temperature probe to a data collector and set it up to collect 18 data points over 180 seconds, or 1 data point every 10 seconds. They heated the end of the probe by placing it in hot water. When it was hot, they set the probe on a table so that the tip was not touching anything, and they began to collect data and record it in the first two columns of the table.

Time (s) t	Temperature (°C) p	$p - L$	$\log(p - L)$
0	29.7495		
10	28.87		
20	27.4995		
30	26.4995		
40	25.812		
50	25.312		
60	24.8745		
70	24.437		
80	24.062		
90	23.8745		
100	23.6245		
110	23.3745		
120	23.187		
130	22.9995		
140	22.812		
150	22.687		
160	22.562		
170	22.437		
180	22.312		

Step 2   Draw a sketch of what you expect the graph of (t, p) data to look like as the temperature probe cooled. Label the axes and mark the scale on your graph. Did everyone in your group draw the same graph? Discuss any differences of opinion.

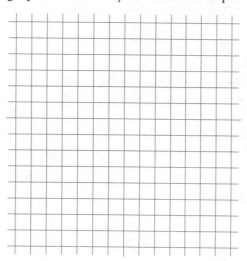

Step 3   Plot the data in the form (t, p) on an appropriately scaled graph. Your graph should appear to be an exponential function. Study the graph and the data, and guess the temperature limit, L.

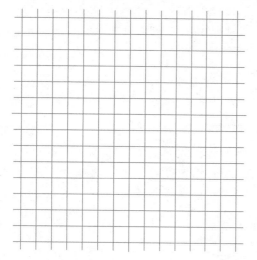

Discovering Advanced Algebra Investigation Worksheets
©2010 Key Curriculum Press

Step 4   Subtract this limit from the temperatures, and record the data in the third column of the table. Find the logarithm of these new data, and complete the last column in the table. Plot data in the form $(t, \log(p - L))$. If the data are not linear, then try a different limit.

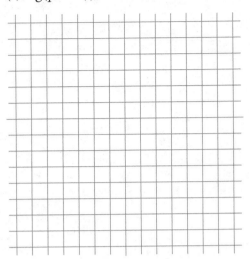

Step 5   Find the equation that models the data in Step 4, and use this to find an equation that models the (t, p) data in Step 3. Give the real-world meanings of the values in the final equation.

Investigation • Chilly Choices

Name_____ **Period**_____ **Date**_____

The school cafeteria offers a choice of ice cream or frozen yogurt for dessert once a week. During the first week of school, 220 students choose ice cream but only 20 choose frozen yogurt. During each of the following weeks, 10% of the frozen-yogurt eaters switch to ice cream and 5% of the ice-cream eaters switch to frozen yogurt.

Step 1 Complete a transition diagram that displays this information.

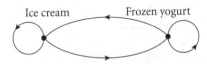

Step 2 Complete a transition matrix that represents this information. The rows should indicate the present condition, and the columns should indicate the next condition after the transition.

Step 3 In the second week, how many students choose ice cream and how many students choose frozen yogurt?

Step 4 How many students will choose each option in the third week?

Step 5   Write a recursive routine to take any week's values and give the next week's values.

Step 6   What do you think will happen to the long-run values of the number of students who choose ice cream and the number who choose frozen yogurt?

Discovering Advanced Algebra Investigation Worksheets
©2010 Key Curriculum Press

Investigation • Find Your Place

Name _____ **Period** _____ **Date** _____

In this investigation you will simulate the weekly movement of rental cars between cities and analyze the results.

Each person represents a rental car starting at City A, City B, or City C.

Step 1 Follow the Procedure Note to simulate the movement of cars. At the beginning of the simulation and after each move, a class recorder should make note of the number of cars at each city.

Procedure Note

Rental Car Simulation

1. All students should position themselves in one of three designated locations in the room, City A, City B, or City C. Report the starting number of cars at each city to the recorder.
2. Use your calculator to generate a random number, x, between 0 and 1. [▶ 🖳 See **Calculator Note 1L** to learn how to generate random numbers.◀] Determine your location for next week as follows:

Starting city	City A		City B		City C	
Next location	$x \leq 0.2$	go to **B**	$x \leq 0.5$ go to **A**	$x \leq 0.1$	go to **B**
	$0.2 < x \leq 0.7$	go to **C**	$x > 0.5$ stay at **B**	$0.1 < x \leq 0.3$	go to **A**
	$x > 0.7$	stay at **A**		$x > 0.3$	stay at **C**

3. On the teacher's signal, you move (or stay) as indicated. Count the number of cars at each city and report this value to the recorder. Repeat the simulation five times. Each time, record the number of cars at each city in the table.

Move	Number of cars City A	Number of cars City B	Number of cars City C
0			
1			
2			
3			
4			
5			

Step 2   Work with your group to make a transition diagram and
a transition matrix that represent the rules of the simulation.

Step 3   Write an initial condition matrix for the starting quantities
at each city. Then, show how to multiply the initial condition
matrix and the transition matrix for the first transition. How do
these theoretical results for week 1 compare with the experimental
data from your simulation?

Step 4   Use your calculator to find the theoretical number of cars at each
city for the next four weeks. Find the theoretical long-run values of
the number of cars at each city. Record your work and results here.

Discovering Advanced Algebra Investigation Worksheets
©2010 Key Curriculum Press

Step 5 Compare these results with the experimental values in your table. If they are not similar, explain why.

Investigation • The Inverse Matrix

Name_____ **Period**_____ **Date**_____

In this investigation you will learn ways to find the inverse of a 2×2 matrix.

Step 1 Use the definition of an inverse matrix to set up a matrix equation. Use these matrices and the 2×2 identity matrix for $[I]$.

$$[A] = \begin{bmatrix} 2 & 1 \\ 4 & 3 \end{bmatrix} \qquad [A]^{-1} = \begin{bmatrix} a & b \\ c & d \end{bmatrix}$$

Step 2 Use matrix multiplication to find the product $[A][A]^{-1}$. Set that product equal to matrix $[I]$.

Step 3 Use the matrix equation from Step 2 to write equations that you can solve to find values for a, b, c, and d. Solve the systems to find the values in the inverse matrix.

Discovering Advanced Algebra Investigation Worksheets
©2010 Key Curriculum Press

Step 4   Use your calculator to find $[A]^{-1}$. If this answer does not match your answer to Step 3, check your work for mistakes. [▶️🔲 See **Calculator Note 6D** to learn how to find the inverse on your calculator.◀]

Step 5   Find the products of $[A][A]^{-1}$ and $[A]^{-1}[A]$. Do they both give you $\begin{bmatrix} 1 & 0 \\ 0 & 1 \end{bmatrix}$? Is matrix multiplication always commutative?

Step 6   Not every square matrix has an inverse. Try to find the inverse of each of these matrices. Make a conjecture about what types of 2×2 square matrices do not have inverses.

a. $\begin{bmatrix} 2 & 1 \\ 4 & 2 \end{bmatrix}$ b. $\begin{bmatrix} 50 & -75 \\ 10 & -15 \end{bmatrix}$ c. $\begin{bmatrix} 10.5 & 1 \\ 31.5 & 3 \end{bmatrix}$ d. $\begin{bmatrix} 2 & 1 \\ 2 & 1 \end{bmatrix}$

Step 7   Can a nonsquare matrix have an inverse? Why or why not?

Investigation • Paying for College

Name _____ **Period** _____ **Date** _____

A total of $40,000 has been donated to a college scholarship fund. The administrators of the fund are considering how much to invest in stocks and how much to invest in bonds. Stocks usually pay more but are often a riskier investment, whereas bonds pay less but are usually safer.

Step 1 Let x represent the amount in dollars invested in stocks, and let y represent the amount in dollars invested in bonds. Graph the equation $x + y = 40{,}000$.

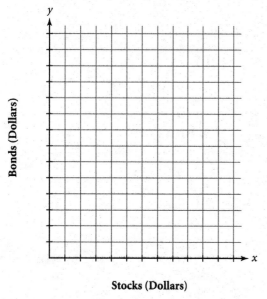

Step 2 Name at least five pairs of x- and y-values that satisfy the inequality $x + y < 40{,}000$ and plot them on your graph. In this problem, why can $x + y$ be less than $40,000?

Step 3 Describe where all possible solutions to the inequality $x + y < 40{,}000$ are located. Shade this region on your graph.

Discovering Advanced Algebra Investigation Worksheets
©2010 Key Curriculum Press

Step 4   Describe some points that fit the condition $x + y \le 40{,}000$ but do not make sense for the situation.

Assume that each option—stocks or bonds—requires a minimum investment of $5,000, and that the fund administrators want to purchase some stocks and some bonds. Based on the advice of their financial advisor, they decide that the amount invested in bonds should be at least twice the amount invested in stocks.

Step 5   Translate all of the limitations, or **constraints,** into a system of inequalities. A table might help you to organize this information.

Step 6   Graph all of the inequalities and determine the region of your graph that will satisfy all the constraints. Find each corner, or **vertex,** of this region.

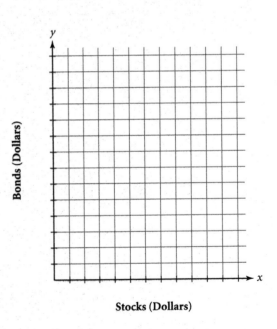

Stocks (Dollars)

Investigation • Maximizing Profit

Name_____ **Period**_____ **Date**_____

The Elite Pottery Shoppe makes two kinds of birdbaths: a fancy glazed and a simple unglazed. An unglazed birdbath requires 0.5 h to make using a pottery wheel and 3 h in the kiln. A glazed birdbath takes 1 h on the wheel and 18 h in the kiln. The company's one pottery wheel is available for at most 8 hours per day (h/d). The three kilns can be used a total of at most 60 h/d, and each kiln can hold only one birdbath. The company has a standing order for 6 unglazed birdbaths per day, so it must produce at least that many. The pottery shop's profit on each unglazed birdbath is $10, and the profit on each glazed birdbath is $40. How many of each kind of birdbath should the company produce each day in order to maximize profit?

Step 1   Organize the information into the table.

	Amount per unglazed birdbath	Amount per glazed birdbath	Constraining value
Wheel hours			
Kiln hours			
Profit			Maximize

Discovering Advanced Algebra Investigation Worksheets
©2010 Key Curriculum Press

Step 2 Use your table to help you write inequalities that reflect the constraints given, and be sure to include any commonsense constraints. Let *x* represent the number of unglazed birdbaths, and let *y* represent the number of glazed birdbaths. Graph the feasible region to show the combinations of unglazed and glazed birdbaths the shop could produce, and label the coordinates of the vertices. (*Note:* Profit is not a constraint; it is what you are trying to maximize.)

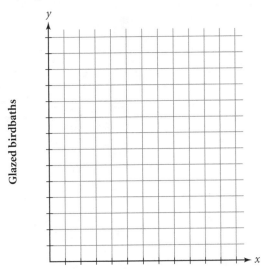

Unglazed birdbaths

Step 3 It will make sense to produce only whole numbers of birdbaths. List the coordinates of all integer points within the feasible region. (There should be 23.) Remember that the feasible region may include points on the boundary lines.

Step 4   Write the equation that will determine profit based on the number of unglazed and glazed birdbaths produced. Calculate the profit that the company would earn at each of the feasible points you found in Step 3. You may want to divide this task among the members of your group.

Step 5   What number of each kind of birdbath should the Elite Pottery Shoppe produce to maximize profit? What is the maximum profit possible? Plot this point on your feasible region graph. What do you notice about this point?

Step 6   Suppose that you want profit to be exactly $100. What equation would express this? Carefully graph this line on your feasible region graph.

Discovering Advanced Algebra Investigation Worksheets
©2010 Key Curriculum Press

Investigation • Maximizing Profit (continued)

Step 7 Suppose that you want profit to be exactly $140. What equation would express this? Carefully add this line to your graph.

Step 8 Suppose that you want profit to be exactly $170. What equation would express this? Carefully add this line to your graph.

Step 9 How do your results from Steps 6–8 show you that (14, 1) must be the point that maximizes profit? Generalize your observations to describe a method that you can use with other problems to find the optimum value. What would you do if this vertex point did not have integer coordinates? What if you wanted to *minimize* profit?

Discovering Advanced Algebra Investigation Worksheets
©2010 Key Curriculum Press

Investigation • Free Fall

Name _____ Period _____ Date _____

You will need: a motion sensor, a small pillow or other
soft object

What function models the height of an object falling due to the force
of gravity? Use a motion sensor to collect data, and analyze the data to
find a function.

Step 1 Follow the Procedure Note to collect data for a falling
object. Let x represent time in seconds, and let y represent
height in meters. Select about 10 points from the free-fall
portion of your data, with x-values forming an arithmetic
sequence. Record this information in the table. Round all
heights to the nearest 0.001.

> **Procedure Note**
> 1. Set the sensor to collect
> distance data approximately
> every 0.05 s for 2 to 5 s.
> [▶ ▣ See **Calculator
> Note 7A** to learn how to
> set up your calculator.◀]
> 2. Place the sensor on the floor.
> Hold a small pillow at a
> height of about 2 m, directly
> above the sensor.
> 3. Start the sensor and drop the
> pillow.

Time (s) x	Height (m) y

Step 2 Use the finite differences method to find the degree of the
polynomial function that models your data. Stop when the
differences are nearly constant.

Investigation • Free Fall (continued)

Step 3   Create scatter plots of the original data (*time, height*), then a scatter plot of (*time, first difference*), and finally a scatter plot of (*time, second difference*). [▸☐ See **Calculator Note 7B** to learn how to calculate finite differences and how to graph them.◂]

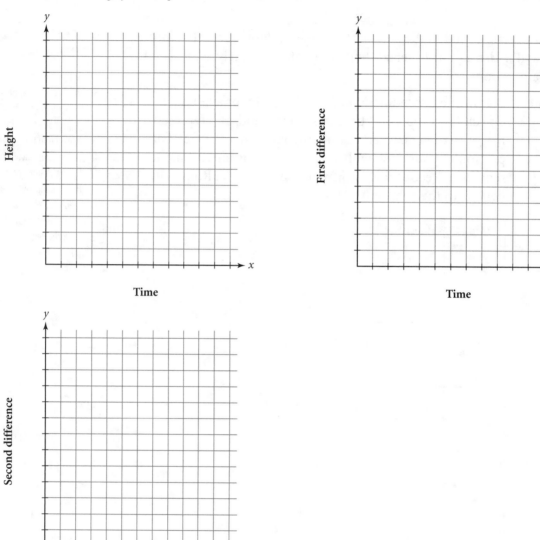

Step 4   Write a description of each graph from Step 3 and what these graphs tell you about the data.

Discovering Advanced Algebra Investigation Worksheets
©2010 Key Curriculum Press

Step 5 Based on your results from using finite differences, what is the degree of the polynomial function that models free fall? Write the general form of this polynomial function.

Step 6 Follow the example on page 380 to write a system of three equations in three variables for your data. Solve your system to find an equation to model the position of a free-falling object dropped from a height of 2 m.

Investigation • Free Fall

Name_____ Period_____ Date_____

What function models the height of an object falling due to the force of gravity? You will use data collected by a motion sensor and analyze the data to find a function.

Step 1 Following the Procedure Note, a motion sensor was used to collect data for a falling object. The heights were rounded to the nearest 0.001 m and recorded in the table below. *x* represents the falling time in seconds, and *y* represents the object's height above the sensor in meters.

Time (s) x	Height (m) y
0.00	2.000
0.05	1.988
0.10	1.951
0.15	1.890
0.20	1.804
0.25	1.694
0.30	1.559
0.35	1.400
0.40	1.216
0.45	1.008

> ### Procedure Note
> 1. Set the sensor to collect distance data approximately every 0.05 s for 2 to 5 s. [▶️🔲] See **Calculator Note 7A** to learn how to set up your calculator.◀]
> 2. Place the sensor on the floor. Hold a small pillow at a height of about 2 m, directly above the sensor.
> 3. Start the sensor and drop the pillow.

Step 2 Use the finite differences method to find the degree of the polynomial function that models the data. Stop when the differences are nearly constant.

Step 3   Create scatter plots of the original data (*time, height*), then a scatter plot of (*time, first difference*), and finally a scatter plot of (*time, second difference*). [▶▢ See **Calculator Note 7B** to learn how to calculate finite differences and how to graph them.◀]

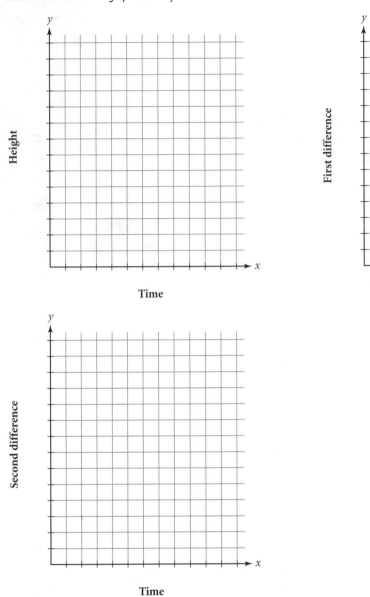

Step 4   Write a description of each graph from Step 3 and what these graphs tell you about the data.

Step 5   Based on your results from using finite differences, what is the degree of the polynomial function that models free fall? Write the general form of this polynomial function.

Step 6   Follow the example on page 380 to write a system of three equations in three variables for the data. Solve your system to find an equation to model the position of a free-falling object dropped from a height of 2 m.

Investigation • Rolling Along

Name _____   **Period** _____   **Date** _____

You will need: a motion sensor, an empty coffee can,
a long table

Step 1   Practice rolling the can up the table directly in front of the
motion sensor. Start the can behind the starting line. Give
the can a gentle push so that it rolls up the table on its own
momentum, stops near the end of the table, and then rolls
back. Stop the can after it crosses the line and before it hits
the motion sensor.

> *Procedure Note*
>
> Prop up one end of the table
> slightly. Place the motion sensor
> at the low end of the table
> and aim it toward the high
> end. With tape or chalk, mark
> a starting line 0.5 m from the
> sensor on the table.

Step 2   Set up your calculator to collect data for 6 seconds.
[▶🖵 See **Calculator Note 7C.** ◀] When the sensor begins, roll the
can up the table.

Step 3   The data collected by the sensor will have the
form (*time, distance*). Adjust for the position
of the starting line by subtracting 0.5 from
each value in the distance list.

Step 4   Let *x* represent time in seconds, and let *y*
represent distance from the line in meters.
Draw a graph of your data below. What shape
is the graph of the data points? What type of
function would model the data? Use finite
differences to justify your answer.

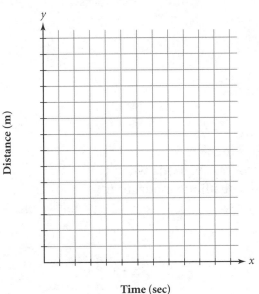

Step 5   Mark the vertex and another point on your graph. Approximate the coordinates of these points and use them to write the equation of a quadratic model in vertex form.

Step 6   From your data, find the distance of the can at 1, 3, and 5 seconds. Use these three data points to find a quadratic model in general form.

Step 7   Mark the *x*-intercepts on your graph. Approximate the values of these *x*-intercepts. Use the zeros and the value of *a* from Step 5 to find a quadratic model in factored form.

Step 8   Verify by graphing that the three equations in Steps 5, 6, and 7 are equivalent, or nearly so. Write a few sentences explaining when you would use each of the three forms to find a quadratic model to fit parabolic data.

Discovering Advanced Algebra Investigation Worksheets
©2010 Key Curriculum Press

Name_____ **Period**_____ **Date**_____

Step 1   Following the Procedure Note, a can was placed directly in front of a motion sensor and behind the starting line. The can was gently pushed so that it rolled up the table on its own momentum, stopped near the end of the table, and then rolled back.

> **Procedure Note**
>
> Prop up one end of the table slightly. Place the motion sensor at the low end of the table and aim it toward the high end. With tape or chalk, mark a starting line 0.5 m from the sensor on the table.

Step 2   A calculator was set to collect data for 6 seconds. When the sensor began, the can was rolled up the table.

Step 3   The data collected by the sensor had the form (*time, distance*).
The distance was adjusted for the position of the starting line by
subtracting 0.5 from each value in the distance list before recording
it in this table.

Time (s) x	Distance from line (m) y	Time (s) x	Distance from line (m) y
0.2	−0.357	3.2	4.257
0.4	−0.355	3.4	4.193
0.6	−0.357	3.6	4.062
0.8	−0.184	3.8	3.871
1.0	0.546	4.0	3.619
1.2	1.220	4.2	3.309
1.4	1.821	4.4	2.938
1.6	2.357	4.6	2.510
1.8	2.825	4.8	2.028
2.0	3.231	5.0	1.493
2.2	3.570	5.2	0.897
2.4	3.841	5.4	0.261
2.6	4.048	5.6	−0.399
2.8	4.188	5.8	−0.426
3.0	4.256	6.0	−0.419

Step 4   Let *x* represent time in seconds, and let *y*
represent distance from the line in meters.
Draw a graph of the data. What shape is the
graph of the data points? What type of function
would model the data? Use finite differences to
justify your answer.

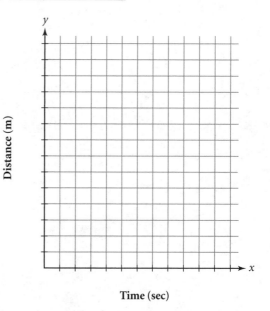

Discovering Advanced Algebra Investigation Worksheets
©2010 Key Curriculum Press

Step 5   Mark the vertex and another point on your graph. Approximate the coordinates of these points and use them to write the equation of a quadratic model in vertex form.

Step 6   From the data, find the distance of the can at 1, 3, and 5 seconds. Use these three data points to find a quadratic model in general form.

Step 7   Mark the *x*-intercepts on your graph. Approximate the values of these *x*-intercepts. Use the zeros and the value of *a* from Step 5 to find a quadratic model in factored form.

Step 8   Verify by graphing that the three equations in Steps 5, 6, and 7 are equivalent, or nearly so. Write a few sentences explaining when you would use each of the three forms to find a quadratic model to fit parabolic data.

Investigation • Complete the Square

Name_____ **Period**_____ **Date**_____

You can use rectangle diagrams to help convert quadratic functions to other equivalent forms.

Step 1 **a.** Complete a rectangle diagram to find the product $(x + 5)(x + 5)$, which can be written $(x + 5)^2$. Write out the four-term polynomial, and then combine any like terms you see and express your answer as a trinomial.

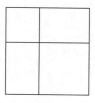

b. What binomial expression is being squared, and what is the perfect-square trinomial represented in this rectangle diagram?

x^2	$-8x$
$-8x$	64

c. Use a rectangle diagram to show the binomial factors for the perfect-square trinomial $x^2 + 24x + 144$.

Discovering Advanced Algebra Investigation Worksheets
©2010 Key Curriculum Press

d. Find the perfect-square trinomial equivalent to $(a + b)^2 = \underline{\ ?\ } + \underline{\ ?\ } + \underline{\ ?\ }$. Describe how you can find the first, second, and third terms of the perfect-square trinomial (written in general form) when squaring a binomial.

Step 2 Consider the expression $x^2 + 6x$.

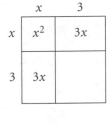

a. What could you add to the expression to make it a perfect square? That is, what must you add to complete this rectangle diagram?

b. If you add a number to an expression, then you must also subtract the same number in order to preserve the value of the original expression. Fill in the blanks to rewrite $x^2 + 6x$ as the difference between a perfect square and a number.

$$x^2 + 6x = x^2 + 6x + \underline{\hspace{2cm}} - \underline{\hspace{2cm}} =$$
$$(x + 3)^2 - \underline{\hspace{2cm}}$$

c. Use a graph or table to verify that your expression in the form $(x - h)^2 + k$ is equivalent to the original expression, $x^2 + 6x$.

Step 3 Consider the expression $x^2 + 6x - 4$.

a. Focus on the 2nd- and 1st-degree terms of the expression, $x^2 + 6x$. What must be added to and subtracted from these terms to complete a perfect square yet preserve the value of the expression?

    b. Rewrite the expression $x^2 + 6x - 4$ in the form $(x - h)^2 + k$.

    c. Use a graph or table to verify that your expression is equivalent to the original expression, $x^2 + 6x - 4$.

Step 4   Rewrite each expression in the form $(x - h)^2 + k$. If you use a rectangle diagram, focus on the 2nd- and 1st-degree terms first. Verify that your expression is equivalent to the original expression.

    a. $x^2 - 14x + 3$ **b.** $x^2 - bx + 10$

When the 2nd-degree term has a coefficient, you can first factor it out of the 2nd- and 1st-degree terms. For example, $3x^2 + 24x + 5$ can be written $3(x^2 + 8x) + 5$. Completing a diagram for $x^2 + 8x$ can help you rewrite the expression in the form $a(x - h)^2 + k$.

$3x^2 + 24x + 5$	Original expression.
$3(x^2 + 8x) + 5$	Factor the 2nd- and 1st-degree terms.
$3(x^2 + 8x + 16) - 3(16) + 5$	Complete the square. You add $3 \cdot 16$, so you must subtract $3 \cdot 16$.
$3(x + 4)^2 - 43$	An equivalent expression in the form $a(x - h)^2 + k$.

	x	4
x	x^2	$4x$
4	$4x$	16

Investigation • Complete the Square (continued)

Step 5   Rewrite each expression in the form $a(x - h)^2 + k$. For Step 5a, use a graph or table to verify that your expression is equivalent to the original expression.

     a. $2x^2 - 6x + 1$ **b.** $ax^2 - 10x + 7$

Step 6   If you graph the quadratic function $y = ax^2 + bx + c$, what will be the x-coordinate of the vertex in terms of a, b, and c? How can you use this value and the equation to find the y-coordinate?

Investigation • How High Can You Go?

Name _____ Period _____ Date _____

Salvador hits a baseball at a height of 3 ft and with an initial upward velocity of 88 feet per second.

Step 1   Let x represent time in seconds after the ball is hit, and let y represent the height of the ball in feet. Write an equation that gives the height as a function of time.

Step 2   Write an equation to find the times when the ball is 24 ft above the ground.

Step 3   Rewrite your equation from Step 2 in the form $ax^2 + bx + c = 0$, then use the quadratic formula to solve. What is the real-world meaning of each of your solutions? Why are there two solutions?

Step 4   Find the y-coordinate of the vertex of this parabola. How many different x-values correspond to this y-value? Explain.

Step 5   Write an equation to find the time when the ball reaches its maximum height. Use the quadratic formula to solve the equation. At what point in the solution process does it become obvious that there is only one solution to this equation?

Step 6   Write an equation to find the time when the ball reaches a height of 200 ft. What happens when you try to solve this impossible situation with the quadratic formula?

Investigation • Complex Arithmetic

Name_____ Period_____ Date_____

When computing with complex numbers, there are conventional rules similar to those you use when working with real numbers. In this investigation you will discover these rules. You may use your calculator to check your work or to explore other examples. [▶️🖥 See **Calculator Note 7E** to learn how to enter complex numbers into your calculator.◀]

Part 1: Addition and Subtraction

Addition and subtraction of complex numbers is similar to combining like terms. Use your calculator to add these complex numbers. Make a conjecture about how to add complex numbers without a calculator.

a. $(2 - 4i) + (3 + 5i)$

b. $(7 + 2i) + (-2 + i)$

c. $(2 - 4i) - (3 + 5i)$

d. $(4 - 4i) - (1 - 3i)$

Part 2: Multiplication

Use your knowledge of multiplying binomials to multiply these complex numbers. Express your products in the form $a + bi$. Recall that $i^2 = -1$.

a. $(2 - 4i)(3 + 5i)$

b. $(7 + 2i)(-2 + i)$

c. $(2 - 4i)^2$

d. $(4 - 4i)(1 - 3i)$

Discovering Advanced Algebra Investigation Worksheets
©2010 Key Curriculum Press

Investigation • Complex Arithmetic (continued)

Part 3: The Complex Conjugates

Recall that every complex number $a + bi$ has a complex conjugate, $a - bi$. Complex conjugates have some special properties and uses.

Each expression below shows either the sum or product of a complex number and its conjugate. Simplify these expressions into the form $a + bi$, and generalize what happens.

a. $(2 - 4i) + (2 + 4i)$

b. $(7 + 2i) + (7 - 2i)$

c. $(2 - 4i)(2 + 4i)$

d. $(-4 + 4i)(-4 - 4i)$

Part 4: Division

Recall that you can create equivalent fractions by multiplying the numerator and denominator of a fraction by the same quantity. For example,
$\frac{3}{4} = \frac{3}{4} \cdot \frac{k}{k} = \frac{3k}{4k}$, and $\frac{3}{\sqrt{2}} \cdot \frac{\sqrt{2}}{\sqrt{2}} = \frac{3\sqrt{2}}{2}$. In the second case, multiplying the fraction $\frac{3}{\sqrt{2}}$ by $\frac{\sqrt{2}}{\sqrt{2}}$ produced an equivalent fraction with an integer denominator instead of an irrational denominator.

You will use a similar technique to change the complex number in each denominator into a real number. Use your work from Part 3 to find a method for changing each denominator into a real number. (Your method should produce an equivalent fraction.) Once you have a real number in the denominator, divide to get an answer in the form $a + bi$.

a. $\frac{7 + 2i}{1 - i}$

b. $\frac{10 - 11i}{4 + 6i}$

c. $\frac{2 - i}{8 - 6i}$

d. $\frac{2 - 4i}{2 + 4i}$

Investigation • The Box Factory

Name _____   **Period** _____   **Date** _____

You will need: the worksheet 16-by-20 Grid Paper,
scissors, tape (optional)

What are the different ways to construct an open-top box from a
16-by-20–unit sheet of material? What is the maximum volume
this box can have? What is the minimum volume? Your group will
investigate this problem by constructing open-top boxes using several
possible integer values for x.

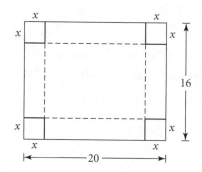

Step 1 Follow the Procedure Note to construct several different-
size boxes from 16-by-20–unit sheets of paper. Record the
dimensions of each box and calculate its volume. Use the
table to record the x-values and volumes of the boxes.

> **Procedure Note**
>
> 1. Cut the 16-by-20–unit rectangles out of the 16-by-20 Grid Paper worksheet.
> 2. Choose several different values for x.
> 3. For each value of x, construct a box by cutting squares with side length x from each corner and folding up the sides.

Length	Width	Height x	Volume y

Step 2 For each box, what are the length, width, and height, in terms of x?
Use these expressions to write a function that gives the volume of a
box as a function of x.

Discovering Advanced Algebra Investigation Worksheets
©2010 Key Curriculum Press

Investigation • The Box Factory (continued)

Step 3   Graph your volume function from Step 2. Plot your data points on the same graph. How do the points relate to the function?

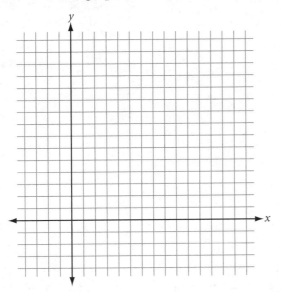

Step 4   What is the degree of this function? Give some reasons to support your answer.

Step 5   Locate the *x*-intercepts of your graph. (There should be three.) Call these three values r_1, r_2, and r_3. Use these values to write the function in the form $y = (x - r_1)(x - r_2)(x - r_3)$.

Step 6   Graph the function from Step 5 with your function from Step 2. What are the similarities and differences between the graphs? How can you alter the function from Step 5 to make both functions equivalent?

Step 7 What happens if you try to make boxes by using the values r_1, r_2, and r_3 as x? What domain of x-values makes sense in this context? What x-value maximizes the volume of the box?

Investigation • The Largest Triangle

Name_____ Period_____ Date_____

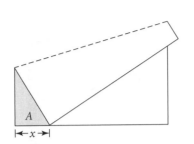 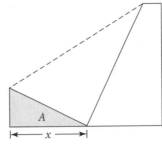

Take a sheet of notebook paper and orient it so that the longest edge is closest to you. Fold the upper-left corner so that it touches some point on the bottom edge. Find the area, *A*, of the triangle formed in the lower-left corner of the paper. What distance, *x*, along the bottom edge of the paper produces the triangle with the greatest area?

Work with your group to find a solution. You may want to use strategies you've learned in several lessons in this chapter. Write a report that explains your solution and your group's strategy for finding the largest triangle. Include any diagrams, tables, or graphs that you used. You might use the sample table and grid provided here.

Distance along bottom (base of triangle) (cm) *x*	Height of triangle (cm)	Area (cm²) *y*

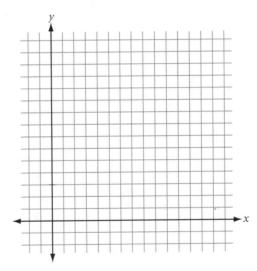

Investigation • Bucket Race

Name _____ **Period** _____ **Date** _____

You will need: the worksheet 1-Centimeter Grid Paper,
a ruler

The starting line of a bucket race is 5 m from one end of a pool, the pool is 20 m long, and the finish line is 7 m from the opposite end of the pool, as shown. In this investigation you will find the shortest path from point *A* to a point *C* on the edge of the pool to point *B*. That is, you will find the value of *x*, the distance in meters from the end of the pool to point *C*, such that $AC + CB$ is the shortest path possible.

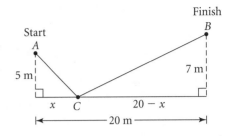

Step 1 Make a scale drawing of the situation on the grid paper.

Step 2 Plot several different locations for point *C*. For each, measure the distance *x* and find the total length $AC + CB$. Record your data in the table.

x (m)	AC (m)	CB (m)	AC + CB (m)

Step 3   What is the best location for *C* such that the length *AC* + *BC* is minimized? What is the distance traveled? Is there more than one best location? Describe at least two different methods for finding the best location for *C*.

Step 4   Make a scale drawing of your solution.

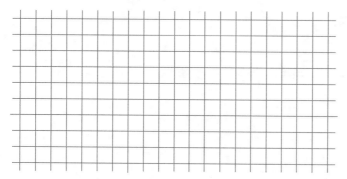

Imagine that the amount of water you empty out at point *B* is an important factor in winning the race. This means you must move carefully so as not to spill water, and you'll be able to move faster with the empty bucket than you can with the bucket full of water. Assume that you can carry an empty bucket at a rate of 1.2 m/s and that you can carry a full bucket, without spilling, at a rate of 0.4 m/s.

Discovering Advanced Algebra Investigation Worksheets
©2010 Key Curriculum Press

Step 5 Go back to the data collected in Step 2 and find the time needed for each x-value. Record the times in the table.

x (m)	Time for AC (s)	Time for CB (s)	Total time (s)

Step 6 Now find the best location for point C so that you minimize the time from point A to the pool edge, and then to point B. What is your minimum time? What is the distance traveled? How does this compare with your answer in Step 3? Describe your solution process.

Investigation • A Slice of Light

Name _____ Period _____ Date _____

You will need: the worksheet $\frac{1}{4}$-Inch Grid Paper,
a flashlight, a relatively dark classroom

The beam of a flashlight is close to the shape of a cone. A sheet of paper held in front of the flashlight shows different slices, or sections, of the cone of light.

Work with a partner, then share results with your group.

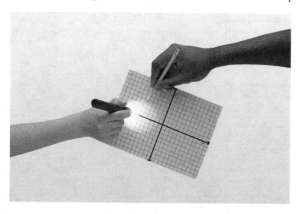

Procedure Note

1. Shine a flashlight on the graph paper at an angle.
2. Align the major axis of the ellipse formed by the beam with one axis of the paper. You might start by placing four points on the paper to help the person holding the flashlight stay on target.
3. Carefully trace the edge of the beam as your partner holds the light steady.

Step 1   Draw a pair of coordinate axes at the center of your graph paper. Follow the Procedure Note and trace an ellipse.

Step 2   Write an equation that fits the data as closely as possible. Find the lengths of both the major and minor axes. Use the values in your equation to locate the foci. Finally, verify your equation by selecting any two pairs of points on the ellipse and checking that the sum of the distances to the foci is constant.

Discovering Advanced Algebra Investigation Worksheets
©2010 Key Curriculum Press

Investigation • A Slice of Light (continued)

Eccentricity is a measure of how elongated an ellipse is. Eccentricity is defined as the ratio $\frac{c}{a}$, for an ellipse with a horizontal major axis, or $\frac{c}{b}$, for an ellipse with a vertical major axis. If the eccentricity is close to 0, then the ellipse looks almost like a circle. The higher the ratio, the more elongated the ellipse.

Step 3 Use your flashlight to make ellipses with different eccentricities. Trace three different ellipses. Calculate the eccentricity of each one and label it on your paper. What is the range of possible values for the eccentricity of an ellipse?

Step 4 Continue to tilt your flashlight until the eccentricity becomes too large and you no longer have an ellipse. What shape can you trace now?

Investigation • Fold a Parabola

Name _____ **Period** _____ **Date** _____

You will need: patty paper, the worksheet $\frac{1}{4}$-Inch Grid
Paper, tape

Fold the patty paper parallel to one edge to form the directrix for a parabola.
Mark a point on the larger portion of the patty paper to serve as the focus
for your parabola. Fold the patty paper so that the focus lies on the directrix.
Unfold, and then fold again, so that the focus is at another point on the
directrix. Repeat this many times. The creases from these folds should create
a parabola.

Lay the patty paper on top of the graph paper, and tape it in place. Identify
the coordinates of the focus and the equation of the directrix, and write an
equation for your parabola.

Discovering Advanced Algebra Investigation Worksheets
©2010 Key Curriculum Press

Investigation • Passing By

Name _____ **Period** _____ **Date** _____

You will need: a motion sensor

Procedure Note

1. One member of your group will use a motion sensor to measure the distance to the walker for 10 s. The motion sensor must be kept pointed at the walker.
2. The walker should start about 5 m to the left of the sensor holder. He or she should walk at a steady pace in a straight line, continuing past the sensor holder, and stop about 5 m to the right of the sensor holder.

Step 1 Collect data as described in the Procedure Note. Transfer these data from the motion sensor to each calculator in the group, and graph your data. They should form one branch of a hyperbola.

Step 2 Assume the sensor was held at the center of the hyperbola, and find an equation to fit your data. You may want to try to graph the asymptotes first.

Step 3   Select approximately 10 representative data points, and graph
them on the grid below. Add the foci and the other branch of the
hyperbola. To verify your equation, choose at least two points on
the curve and measure their distances from the foci. Calculate the
differences between the distances from each focus. What do you
notice? Why?

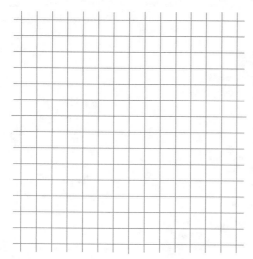

Investigation • Passing By

Name_____ Period_____ Date_____

Step 1   The Procedure Note was followed to collect the data in this table. Enter these values in your calculator, and graph them. They should form one branch of a hyperbola.

Time (s)	Distance (m)	Time (s)	Distance (m)
0	5.000	3.8	0.926
0.2	4.720	4.0	0.966
0.4	4.381	4.2	1.056
0.6	4.016	4.4	1.240
0.8	3.688	4.6	1.387
1.0	3.558	4.8	1.568
1.2	3.302	5.0	1.673
1.4	3.078	5.2	1.978
1.6	2.709	5.4	2.251
1.8	2.410	5.6	2.478
2.0	2.249	5.8	2.748
2.2	1.969	6.0	3.099
2.4	1.770	6.2	3.284
2.6	1.605	6.4	3.533
2.8	1.525	6.6	3.820
3.0	1.291	6.8	4.116
3.2	1.022	7.0	4.379
3.4	0.901	7.2	4.695
3.6	0.882	7.4	4.955

Step 2   Assume the sensor was held at the center of the hyperbola, and find an equation to fit the data. You may want to try to graph the asymptotes first.

Step 3   Select approximately 10 representative data points, and graph them on the grid below. Add the foci and the other branch of the hyperbola. To verify your equation, choose at least two points on the curve and measure their distances from the foci. Calculate the differences between the distances from each focus. What do you notice? Why?

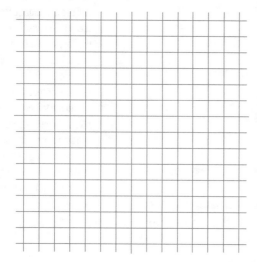

Discovering Advanced Algebra Investigation Worksheets
©2010 Key Curriculum Press

Investigation • Systems of Conic Equations

Name_____   Period_____   Date_____

If you graph two conic sections on the same graph, in how many ways could they intersect?

There are four conic sections: circles, ellipses, parabolas, and hyperbolas. Among the members of your group, investigate the possible numbers of intersection points for all ten pairs of shapes. For example, an ellipse and a hyperbola could intersect in 0, 1, 2, 3, or 4 points, as shown below. For each pair of conic sections, list the possible numbers of intersection points.

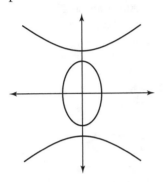

0 intersections

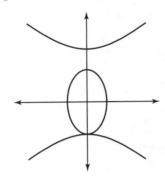

1 intersection

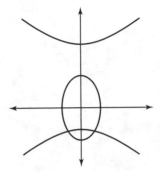

2 intersections

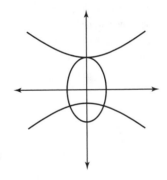

3 intersections

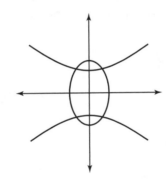

4 intersections

Investigation • The Breaking Point

Name _____ **Period** _____ **Date** _____

You will need: several pieces of dry linguine, a small film canister, string, some weights (pennies, beans, or other small units of mass), a ruler, tape

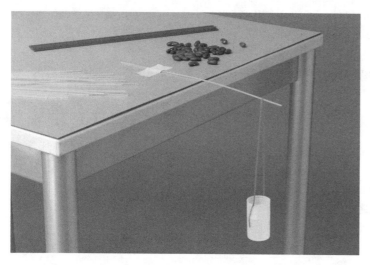

Procedure Note

1. Lay a piece of linguine on a table so that its length is perpendicular to one side of the table and the end extends over the edge of the table.
2. Tie the string to the film canister so that you can hang it from the end of the linguine. (You may need to use tape to hold the string in place.)
3. Measure the length of the linguine between the edge of the table and the string. (See the photo.) Record this information in a table of (*length, mass*) data.
4. Place mass units into the container one at a time until the linguine breaks. Record the maximum number of weights that the length of linguine was able to support.

Step 1 Work with a partner. Follow the Procedure Note to record at least five data points, and then compile your results with those of other group members.

Length (cm) x	Mass (number of weights) y

Discovering Advanced Algebra Investigation Worksheets
©2010 Key Curriculum Press

Step 2 Make a graph of your data with length as the independent variable, *x*, and mass as the dependent variable, *y*. Does the relationship appear to be linear? If not, describe the appearance of the graph.

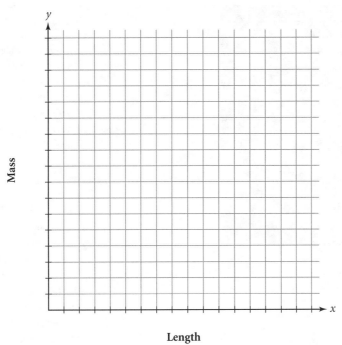

The relationship between length and mass is an **inverse variation.** The parent function for an inverse variation curve, $f(x) = \frac{1}{x}$, is the simplest **rational function.**

Step 3 Your data should fit a dilated version of the parent function $f(x) = \frac{1}{x}$. Write an equation that is a good fit for the plotted data.

Investigation • The Breaking Point

With Sample Data

Name_____ Period_____ Date_____

Procedure Note

1. Lay a piece of linguine on a table so that its length is perpendicular to one side of the table and the end extends over the edge of the table.

2. Tie the string to the film canister so that you can hang it from the end of the linguine. (You may need to use tape to hold the string in place.)

3. Measure the length of the linguine between the edge of the table and the string. (See the photo.) Record this information in a table of (*length, mass*) data.

4. Place mass units into the container one at a time until the linguine breaks. Record the maximum number of weights that the length of linguine was able to support.

Step 1 Students in a mathematics class followed the Procedure Note to collect the data recorded in this table. They used pennies as weights.

Length (cm) x	Mass (number of pennies) y
16	6
16	5
15	7
15	6
14	6
13	7
13	6
12	8
12	7
11	8
10	9
9	10
8	11
7	13
6	16

Step 2 Make a graph of these data with length as the independent variable, x, and mass as the dependent variable, y. Does the relationship appear to be linear? If not, describe the appearance of the graph.

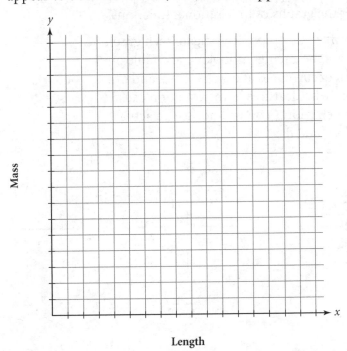

Length

The relationship between length and mass is an **inverse variation.**
The parent function for an inverse variation curve, $f(x) = \frac{1}{x}$, is the simplest
rational function.

Step 3 Your data should fit a dilated version of the parent function
$f(x) = \frac{1}{x}$. Write an equation that is a good fit for the plotted data.

Investigation • Predicting Asymptotes and Holes

Name_____   Period_____   Date_____

In this investigation you will consider the graphs of four rational functions.

Step 1   Match each rational function with a graph. Investigate each graph by dragging a point on the graph, tracing, or looking at a table of values. Describe the unusual occurrences at exactly $x = 2$ and other values nearby. Try to explain what features in the equation cause the different types of graph behavior. (You will not see an actual "hole," as pictured in graphs b and d.)

a.
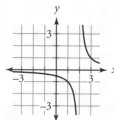

b.
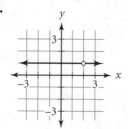

c.
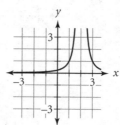

d.
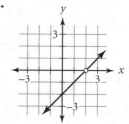

A. $y = \dfrac{1}{(x-2)^2}$

B. $y = \dfrac{1}{x-2}$

C. $y = \dfrac{(x-2)^2}{x-2}$

D. $y = \dfrac{x-2}{x-2}$

_____   _____   _____   _____

Discovering Advanced Algebra Investigation Worksheets
©2010 Key Curriculum Press

Investigation • Predicting Asymptotes and Holes (continued)

Step 2   Have each group member choose one of the graphs below.
Find a rational function equation for your graph, and write a few
sentences that explain the appearance of your graph. Share your
answers with your group.

a. 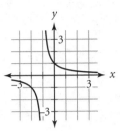   **b.** 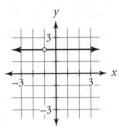   **c.** 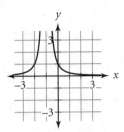   **d.**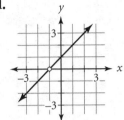

_____   _____   _____   _____

Step 3   Write a paragraph explaining how you can use an equation
to predict where holes and asymptotes will occur, and how you
can use these features in a graph to write an equation.

Step 4   Consider the graph of $y = \frac{x-2}{(x-2)^2}$. What features does it have? What
can you generalize about the graph of a function that has a factor
that occurs more times in the denominator than in the numerator?

Investigation • Arithmetic Series Formula

Name _____ **Period** _____ **Date** _____

You will need: the worksheet 1-Centimeter Grid Paper,
scissors

In this investigation you will use a geometric model to help you develop an explicit formula for the partial sum of an arithmetic series.

Step 1 The lengths of the rows of this step-shaped figure represent terms of an arithmetic sequence. Write the sequence u_1, u_2, u_3, u_4, u_5, represented by the figure. What is the sum of the series?

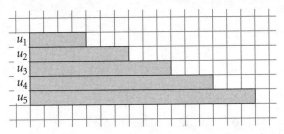

Step 2 If you cut out two copies of this figure and slid them together to make a rectangle, what would the dimensions of your rectangle be?

Step 3 Have each member of your group create a different arithmetic sequence. Each of you can choose a starting value and a common difference. (Use positive numbers less than 10 for each of these.) On the grid paper, draw two copies of a step-shaped figure representing your sequence.

Investigation • Arithmetic Series Formula (continued)

Step 4   Cut out both copies of the step-shaped figure. Slide the two congruent shapes together to form a rectangle, and then calculate the dimensions and area of the rectangle. Now express this area in terms of the number of rows, n, and the first and last terms of the sequence.

Step 5   Based on what you have discovered, what is a formula for the partial sum, S_n, of an arithmetic series? Describe the relationship between your formula and the dimensions of your rectangle.

Discovering Advanced Algebra Investigation Worksheets
©2010 Key Curriculum Press

Investigation • Infinite Geometric Series Formula

Name_____ Period_____ Date_____

You may have learned a method for writing a repeating decimal as a fraction. This method can also help you find the value of an infinite geometric series.

For example, consider the repeating decimal $0.44444\ldots$. It can be thought of as the sum of the infinite geometric series $0.4 + 0.04 + 0.004 + \cdots$. If $S = 0.44444\ldots$, then $10S = 4.44444\ldots$. Subtract $10S - S$ to eliminate the decimal portion:

$$10S = 4.44444\ldots$$
$$\underline{-S = 0.44444\ldots}$$
$$9S = 4$$

Solving for S gives $S = \frac{4}{9}$, so the series $0.4 + 0.04 + 0.004 + \cdots$ has sum $\frac{4}{9}$.

Step 1 Consider the sequence $0.4, 0.04, 0.004, \ldots$ underlying the series S. Identify the first term, u_1, and the common ratio, r, of the sequence. How is the multiplier 10 (in the expression $10S$) derived from r? What other multipliers could be used to eliminate the repeating decimal portion?

Step 2 Use the common ratio, r, as the multiplier instead of 10 and solve for S again. Is your answer equivalent to $\frac{4}{9}$?

Step 3 Consider the sequence $0.9, 0.09, 0.009, \ldots$. Identify the first term, u_1, and the common ratio, r. Now use the method from Step 2 to find the sum S of the series $0.9 + 0.09 + 0.009 + \cdots$.

Step 4   Repeat Step 3 for the sequence 0.27, 0.0027, 0.000027, ...
Remember to use r as the multiplier.

Step 5   Repeat Step 3 for the series $u_1 + r \cdot u_1 + r^2 \cdot u_1 + r^3 \cdot u_1 + \cdots$,
assuming that it has sum S. Create a new series with sum $r \cdot S$.
Then subtract to find a formula for S based on u_1 and r.

Step 6   Use a variety of r-values, including both positive and negative
numbers, to create several geometric sequences. Look at the partial
sums of each sequence as n gets very large. Use your formula from
Step 5 to help you describe when the partial sums of a geometric
sequence will converge to a unique number S. Use your examples
to justify your answer.

Discovering Advanced Algebra Investigation Worksheets
©2010 Key Curriculum Press

Investigation • Geometric Series Formula

Name _____ **Period** _____ **Date** _____

A ball is dropped from 180 cm above the floor. With each bounce, it rebounds to 65% of its previous height.

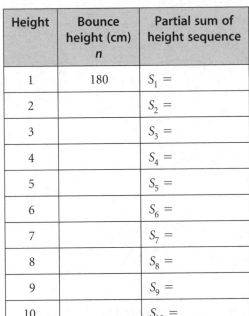

Step 1   Use your calculator to find the first ten heights, with the initial drop height being the first term of the sequence. Then find the first ten partial sums of this sequence of heights: $S_1, S_2, S_3, \ldots, S_{10}$. Record the values in this table.

Height	Bounce height (cm) n	Partial sum of height sequence
1	180	$S_1 =$
2		$S_2 =$
3		$S_3 =$
4		$S_4 =$
5		$S_5 =$
6		$S_6 =$
7		$S_7 =$
8		$S_8 =$
9		$S_9 =$
10		$S_{10} =$

Step 2   Create a scatter plot of points (n, S_n) and find a translated exponential equation to fit the data. Sketch the scatter plot on the grid below. The equation will be in the form $S_n = L - a \cdot b^n$. (*Hint: L* is the long-run value of the partial sums.)

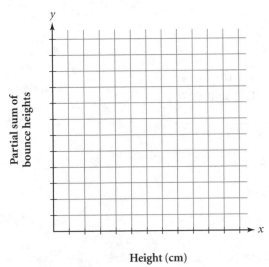

Height (cm)

Investigation • Geometric Series Formula (continued)

Step 3   Rewrite your equation from Step 2 in terms of n, a or u_1, and r. Use algebraic techniques to write your explicit formula as a single rational expression.

Step 4   Here is a way to arrive at an equivalent formula. Complete the derivation by filling in the blanks.

$$S_n = u_1 + u_1 \cdot r + u_1 \cdot r^2 + \cdots + u_1 \cdot r^{n-1}$$

$$rS_n = \underline{\hspace{4cm}}$$

$$S_n - rS_n = \underline{\hspace{4cm}}$$

$$S_n = \underline{\hspace{4cm}}$$

Use algebraic techniques to verify that the formula is equivalent to your formula from Step 3.

Step 5   Use your formula from Step 4 to find S_{10} for the bouncing ball. Then use it to find S_{10} for the geometric sequence $2, 6, 18, 54, \ldots$.

Discovering Advanced Algebra Investigation Worksheets
©2010 Key Curriculum Press

Investigation • Flip a Coin

Name _____ Period _____ Date _____

You will need: a coin

In this investigation you will explore the predictability of random outcomes. You will use a familiar random process, the flip of a coin.

Step 1 Imagine you are flipping a **fair** coin, one that is equally likely to land heads or tails. Without flipping a coin, record a random arrangement of H's and T's, as though you were flipping a coin ten times. This is Sequence A.

Sequence A (imagined sequence)										
Sequence B (actual sequence)										

Step 2 Now flip a coin ten times and record the results on the second line. This is Sequence B.

Step 3 How is Sequence A different from the result of your coin flips? Make at least two observations.

Investigation • Flip a Coin (continued)

Step 4 Find the longest string of consecutive H's or T's in Sequence A. Do the same for Sequence B. Then find the second-longest string. Record these lengths for each person in the class as tally marks in the table below. How do the lengths of the longest strings in Sequence A compare with the lengths of the longest strings in Sequence B?

Longest string	Sequence A	Sequence B	2nd-longest string	Sequence A	Sequence B
1			1		
2			2		
3			3		
4			4		
5 or more			5 or more		

Discovering Advanced Algebra Investigation Worksheets
©2010 Key Curriculum Press

Investigation • Flip a Coin (continued)

Step 5   Count the number of H's in each set. Record the results of the entire class in the table at right. What do you notice about the numbers of H's in Sequence A compared with Sequence B?

Number of H's	Sequence A	Sequence B
0		
1		
2		
3		
4		
5		
6		
7		
8		
9		
10		

Step 6   If you were asked to write a new random sequence of H's and T's, how would it be different from what you recorded in Sequence A?

Investigation • The Multiplication Rule

Name_____ **Period**_____ **Date**_____

Step 1 Refer to the tree diagram (shown below) for Example A, part a. Write the probability on each branch. Then find the probability of each path.

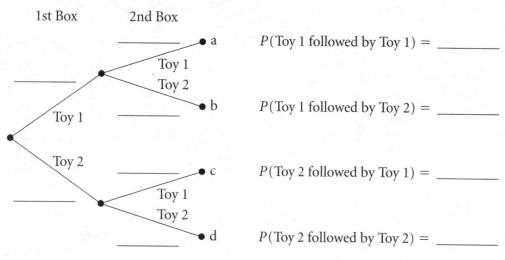

$P(\text{Toy 1 followed by Toy 1}) = $ _____

$P(\text{Toy 1 followed by Toy 2}) = $ _____

$P(\text{Toy 2 followed by Toy 1}) = $ _____

$P(\text{Toy 2 followed by Toy 2}) = $ _____

Step 2 Redraw the tree diagram for Example A, part b. Indicate the probability on each branch, and also write the probability of each path. What is the sum of the probabilities of all possible paths? What is the sum of the probabilities of the highlighted paths?

Discovering Advanced Algebra Investigation Worksheets
©2010 Key Curriculum Press

Step 3   Suppose the national advertisement mentioned in Example A listed four different toys distributed equally in a huge supply of boxes. Draw only as much of a tree diagram as you need to in order to answer these questions:

a. What would be $P(\text{Toy 2})$ in Talya's first box? Talya's second box? Third box? $P(\text{any particular toy in any particular box})$?

b. In these situations, does the toy she finds in one box influence the probability of there being a particular toy in the next box?

    c. One outcome that includes all four toys is Toy 3, followed by Toy 2, followed by Toy 4, followed by Toy 1. What is the probability of this outcome? Another outcome would be the same four toys in a different order. How many such outcomes are there? Are they all equally likely?

Step 4   Write a statement explaining how to use the probabilities of a path's branches to find the probability of the path.

Step 5   What is P(obtaining the complete set in the first four boxes)?

Discovering Advanced Algebra Investigation Worksheets
©2010 Key Curriculum Press

Investigation • Addition Rule

Name _____ **Period** _____ **Date** _____

Of the 100 students in 12th grade, 70 are enrolled in mathematics, 50 are in science, 30 are in both subjects, and 10 are in neither subject.

Step 1 "A student takes mathematics" and "a student takes science" are two events. Are these events mutually exclusive? Explain.

Step 2 Complete the Venn diagram below to show enrollments in mathematics and science courses.

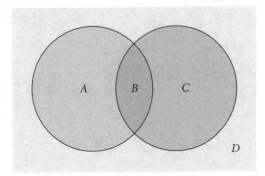

Step 3 Use the numbers of students in your Venn diagram to calculate probabilities.

Step 4 Explain why the probability that a randomly chosen student takes mathematics or science, $P(M \text{ or } S)$, does not equal $P(M) + P(S)$.

Step 5 Create a formula for calculating $P(M \text{ or } S)$ that includes the expressions $P(M)$, $P(S)$, and $P(M \text{ and } S)$.

Step 6   Suppose two dice are tossed. Draw a Venn diagram to represent the events

   A = "sum is 7"

   B = "both dice > 2"

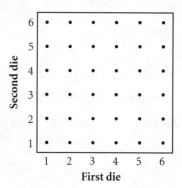

Find the probabilities in parts a–e by counting dots:

a. $P(A)$

b. $P(B)$

c. $P(A \text{ and } B)$

d. $P(A \text{ or } B)$

e. $P(\text{not } A \text{ and not } B)$

f. Find $P(A \text{ or } B)$ by using a rule or formula similar to your response in Step 5.

Step 7   Complete the statement: For any two events A and B,

   $P(A \text{ or } B) =$ _____.

Discovering Advanced Algebra Investigation Worksheets
©2010 Key Curriculum Press

Investigation • "Dieing" for a Four

Name _____ **Period** _____ **Date** _____

You will need: a die

Each person will need a single die. [▶🖳 See **Calculator Note 1L** to simulate rolling a die if you don't have one.◀] Imagine that you're about to play a board game in which you must roll a 4 on your die before taking your first turn.

Step 1   Record the number of rolls it takes for you to get a 4. Repeat this a total of ten times. Combine your results with those of your group and find the mean of all values. Then find the mean of all the group results in the class.

Number of rolls to get a 4										

Mean for group: _____

Mean for all groups: _____

Step 2   Based on this experiment, how many rolls would you expect to make on average before a 4 comes up?

Step 3   To calculate the result theoretically, imagine a "perfect" sequence of rolls, with the results 1, 2, 3, 4, 5, 6, 1, 2, 3, 4, 5, 6, and so on. On average, how many rolls do you need after each 4 to get the next 4?

Step 4   Another theoretical approach uses the fact that the probability of success is $\frac{1}{6}$. Calculate the probability of rolling the first 4 on the first roll, the first 4 on the second roll, the first 4 on the third roll, and the first 4 on the fourth roll. (A tree diagram might help you do the calculations.)

Step 5   Find a formula for the probability of rolling the first 4 on the nth roll.

Step 6   Create a spreadsheet column or a calculator list with the numbers 1 through 100. Use your formula from Step 5 to make a second list of the probabilities of rolling the first 4 on the first roll, the second roll, the third roll, and so on, up to the 100th roll. Create a third list that is the product of these two lists. Calculate the sum of this third list. [▶🔲 See **Calculator Note 2A.**◀]

Step 7   How close is the sum you found in Step 6 to your estimates in Steps 2 and 3?

Investigation • Name That Tune

Name_____   Period_____   Date_____

Suppose you want to create a random playlist from a library of songs on an MP3 player. If you do not repeat any songs, in how many different orders do you think the songs could be played? In this investigation you will discover a pattern allowing you to determine the number of possible orders without listing all of them.

Step 1   Start by investigating some simple cases. Consider libraries of up to five songs, and playlists of up to five of those songs. In the table, n represents the number of songs in the library ($1 \le n \le 5$) and r represents the length of the playlist ($1 \le r \le n$). For example, $n = 3$ and $r = 2$ represents the number of playlists you can make using two songs from a library of three songs. Let A, B, and C represent the three songs available. The two-song playlists that don't repeat songs are AB, AC, BA, BC, CA, and CB. So there are six playlists.

Complete the table for different values of n and r.

		Number of songs in library, n			
	$n = 1$	$n = 2$	$n = 3$	$n = 4$	$n = 5$
$r = 1$					
$r = 2$			6		
$r = 3$					
$r = 4$					
$r = 5$					

(Row label: Number of songs in playlists, r)

Step 2   Compare your results with those of your group. Describe any patterns you found in either the rows or columns of the table.

Step 3   Use the patterns you found in the table to write an expression for the number of ways to arrange 10 songs in a playlist from a library of 150 songs.

Investigation • Winning the Lottery

Name_____ **Period**_____ **Date**_____

You will do Step 1 of this investigation with the whole class. Then, in Steps 2–8, you will work with your group to analyze the results.

Consider a state lottery called Lotto 47. Twice a week, players select six different numbers between 1 and 47. The state lottery commission also selects six numbers between 1 and 47. Selection order doesn't matter, but a player needs to match all six numbers to win Lotto 47.

Step 1 Follow these directions with your class to simulate playing Lotto 47.

   a. For five minutes, write down as many sets of six different numbers as you can. Write only integers between 1 and 47.

   b. After five minutes of writing, everyone stands up.

   c. Your teacher will generate a random integer, 1–47. Cross out all of your sets of six numbers that do not contain the given number. If you cross out all of your sets, sit down.

   d. Your teacher will generate a second number, 1–47. (If it's the same number as before, it will be skipped.) Again, cross out all of your sets that do not contain this number. If you cross out all of your sets, sit down.

Discovering Advanced Algebra Investigation Worksheets
©2010 Key Curriculum Press

Investigation • Winning the Lottery (continued)

> **e.** Your teacher will continue generating different random numbers until no one is still standing or six numbers have been generated.

Work with your group to answer the questions in Steps 2–8.

Step 2 What is the probability that any one set of six numbers wins?

Step 3 At $1 for each set of six numbers, how much did each of your group members invest during the first five minutes? What was the total group investment?

Step 4 Estimate the total amount invested by the entire class during the first five minutes. Explain how you determined this estimate.

Step 5 Estimate the probability that someone in your class wins. Explain how you determined this estimate.

Step 6 Estimate the probability that someone in your school would win if everyone in the school participated in this activity. Explain how you determined this estimate.

Investigation • Winning the Lottery (continued)

Step 7   If each possible set of six numbers were written on a 1-inch chip and if all the chips were laid end to end, how long would the line of chips be? Convert your answer to an appropriate unit.

Step 8   Write a paragraph comparing Lotto 47 with some other event whose probability is approximately the same.

Discovering Advanced Algebra Investigation Worksheets
©2010 Key Curriculum Press

Investigation • Pascal's Triangle and Combination Numbers

Name _____ Period _____ Date _____

A group of five students regularly eats lunch together, but each day only three of them can show up.

Step 1 How many groups of three students could there be? Express your answer in the form $_nC_r$ and as a numeral.

Step 2 If Leora is definitely at the table, how many other students are at the table? How many students are there to choose from? Find the number of combinations of students possible in this instance. Express your answer in the form $_nC_r$ and as a numeral.

Step 3 How many three-student combinations are there that don't include Leora? Consider how many students there are to select from and how many are to be chosen. Express your answer in the form $_nC_r$ and as a numeral.

Step 4 Repeat Steps 1–3 for groups of four of the five students.

Step 5 What patterns do you notice in your answers to Steps 1–3 for groups of three students and four students? Write a general rule that expresses $_nC_r$ as a sum of other combination numbers.

Step 6 How does this rule relate to Pascal's triangle (shown below)?

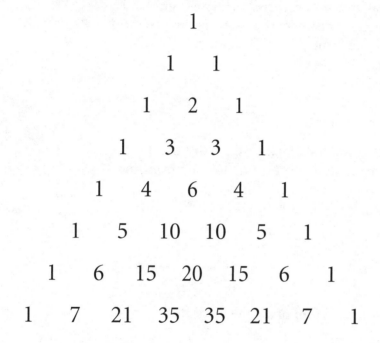

Discovering Advanced Algebra Investigation Worksheets

Investigation • Designing a Study

Name _____ **Period** _____ **Date** _____

Consider this hypothesis: Listening to music while doing math homework will shorten the time it takes to complete the assignment.

Your group will design two studies that could test this hypothesis. Choose two of the types of study described in this lesson, and describe how you would collect sample data for the study. Provide enough detail so that another group could use your description to collect data in the same way. Keep in mind these points as you design your study:

- If you design an **experiment,** you must describe what treatments will be used and how subjects will be assigned to a treatment.

- To design an **observational study,** you must describe what is to be observed and measured and how you'll decide which subjects to observe.

- A **survey** plan must address who will be surveyed, the method of survey (interview, paper questionnaire, e-mail, and so on), and the exact questions to be asked.

Investigation • Pencil Lengths

Name_____ **Period**_____ **Date**_____

You will need: centimeter rulers, a few pencils

In this investigation you'll explore the difference between discrete and continuous random variables.

Begin by collecting all the pencils that your group has.

Step 1   Measure your pencils accurate to a tenth of a centimeter. Before you share data with other groups, predict the shape of a histogram of the class data.

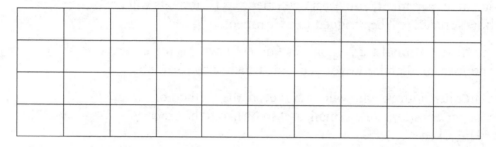

Step 2   Share all measurements so that the class has one set of data. Draw a histogram with bins representing 1 cm increments in pencil length.

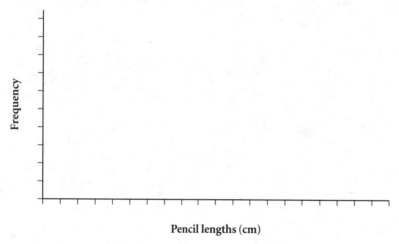

Pencil lengths (cm)

Discovering Advanced Algebra Investigation Worksheets
©2010 Key Curriculum Press

Investigation • Pencil Lengths (continued)

Step 3 Divide the number of pencils in each bin by the total number of pencils. Make a new histogram, using these quotients as the values on the *y*-axis.

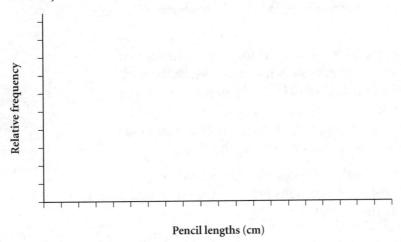

Step 4 Check that the area of your second histogram is 1. Why must this be true?

Step 5 Imagine that you collect more and more pencils and draw a histogram using the method described in Step 3. Sketch what this histogram of increasingly many pencil lengths would look like. Give reasons for your answer.

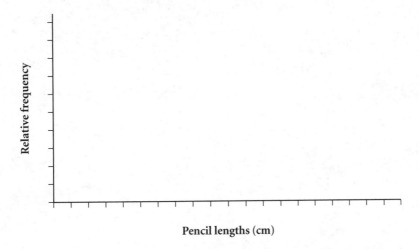

Step 6   Imagine doing a very complete and precise survey of all the pencils
in the world. Assume that their distribution is about the same as
the distribution of pencils in your sample. Also assume that you
use infinitely many very narrow bins. What will this histogram look
like?

To approximate this plot, sketch over the top of your histogram
in Step 5 with a smooth curve, as shown at right. Make the area
between the curve and the horizontal axis about the same as the
area of the histogram. Make sure that the extra area enclosed by
the curve above the histogram is about the same as the area cut
off the corners of the bins as you smooth out the shape.

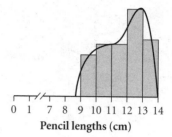

Pencil lengths (cm)

Step 7   Let x represent pencil length. Use your histogram from Step 6
to estimate the areas of various regions between the curve and
the x-axis that satisfy these conditions:

a. $x < 10$

b. $11 < x < 12$

c. $x > 12.5$

d. $x = 11$

Discovering Advanced Algebra Investigation Worksheets
©2010 Key Curriculum Press

Investigation • Pencil Lengths

With Sample Data

Name _____   Period _____   Date _____

In this investigation you'll explore the difference between discrete and continuous random variables.

Students began the investigation by collecting all the pencils their group had.

Step 1   The groups measured their pencils accurate to a tenth of a centimeter. They shared all their measurements so that the class had the data recorded in the table.

16.9	18.7	11.3	13.8	15.2	17	16.5	16.6	11.8	17.2
15.5	15.7	17	11.4	16.5	16	13.4	15.7	15.5	14.1
12.3	13.8	15.5	15.7	10.7	15.6	12.1	14.4	16.5	17.9
8.2	17.8	17.6	14.1	16.7	14.6	12.3	10	13.2	14.3

Step 2   Draw a histogram with bins representing 1 cm increments in pencil length.

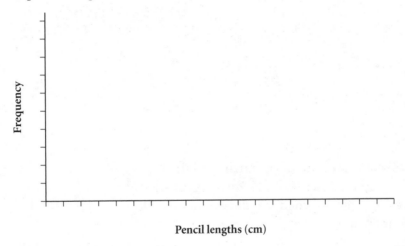

Pencil lengths (cm)

Step 3   Divide the number of pencils in each bin by the total number of
pencils. Make a new histogram, using these quotients as the values
on the *y*-axis.

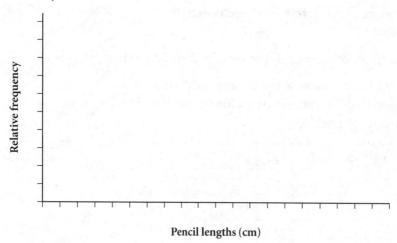

Step 4   Check that the area of your second histogram is 1. Why must this
be true?

Step 5   Imagine that you collect more and more pencils and draw a
histogram using the method described in Step 3. Sketch what this
histogram of increasingly many pencil lengths would look like.
Give reasons for your answer.

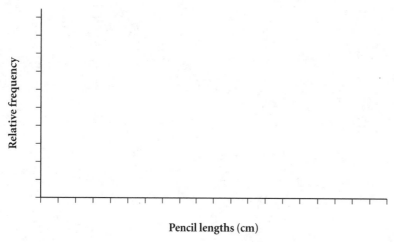

Step 6   Imagine doing a very complete and precise survey of all the pencils in the world. Assume that their distribution is about the same as the distribution of pencils in the sample. Also assume that you use infinitely many very narrow bins. What will this histogram look like?

To approximate this plot, sketch over the top of your histogram in Step 5 with a smooth curve, as shown at right. Make the area between the curve and the horizontal axis about the same as the area of the histogram. Make sure that the extra area enclosed by the curve above the histogram is about the same as the area cut off the corners of the bins as you smooth out the shape.

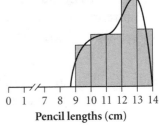

Pencil lengths (cm)

Step 7   Let x represent pencil length. Use your histogram from Step 6 to estimate the areas of various regions between the curve and the x-axis that satisfy these conditions:

    a. $x < 10$

    b. $11 < x < 12$

    c. $x > 12.5$

    d. $x = 11$

Investigation • The Normal Curve

Name_____ **Period**_____ **Date**_____

Imagine that a group of students finds the weights of 500 U.S. pennies. Even if the actual weights of the pennies were exactly the same, there would be some variation in the measurements of those weights. Typically, the measurements made by a group of people of the same or very similar objects are normally distributed. You'll use this idea to explore areas under the normal curve.

Step 1 Each person in your group should use technology to simulate the weights of 500 pennies. Technically, this is a sample from a population of infinitely many weights. Assume that pennies are normally distributed about a mean of 2.5 g and have a standard deviation of 0.14 g. [▶️🖥 See **Calculator Note 11D.**◀]

Step 2 Create a histogram of your own data set using a bin width equal to the standard deviation and with the leftmost bin edge at $\mu - 4\sigma = 1.94$. What percentage of your sample is within one standard deviation of the mean weight? That is, what percentage of the sample is between $2.5 - 0.14 = 2.36$ g and $2.5 + 0.14 = 2.64$ g?

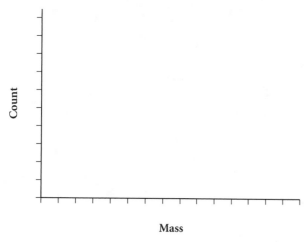

Step 3 What percentage of your sample is within two standard deviations of the mean weight? Within three standard deviations of the mean weight?

Discovering Advanced Algebra Investigation Worksheets
©2010 Key Curriculum Press

Step 4 There is a rule in statistics known as the "68-95-99.7 rule." Compare your results from Steps 2 and 3 with those of your group, and write a rule that might go by this name.

Step 5 Each person in your group should select a different mean and positive standard deviation for a normal distribution. Use your calculators to find the probability that a value lies within one, two, and three standard deviations of the mean. [▶☐ See **Calculator Note 11C** for help finding the area of a region under the normal curve. ◀]

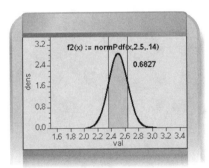 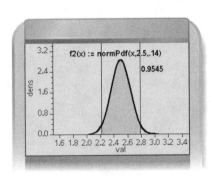 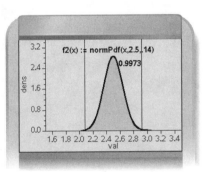

Step 6 Summarize the results of your group for Step 5. Do the probabilities follow the 68-95-99.7 rule?

Investigation • Keeping Score

Name_____ **Period**_____ **Date**_____

Andres and his cousin Imani have always been very competitive. This year they are both taking French at their respective schools. Andres boasted that he scored 86 on a recent exam. Imani had scored only 84 on her latest exam. But she countered by asking Andres about the mean and standard deviation on his test. The mean score on Andres's exam was 74 and the standard deviation was 9. The mean score on Imani's exam was 75 and the standard deviation was 6. Which of the two scores was actually better relative to the population of scores on the same exam?

Work with your group to decide who has the better score. Come up with a measure that uses the mean and standard deviation to support your conclusion. Be prepared to explain your measure and justify your conclusion.

Discovering Advanced Algebra Investigation Worksheets
©2010 Key Curriculum Press

Investigation • Looking for Connections

Name _____ **Period** _____ **Date** _____

Step 1   Work with your group to create a survey with five questions that are all answered with a number, or use the sample survey here.

1. How many minutes of homework did you do last night?

2. How many minutes did you spend talking, calling, e-mailing, or writing to friends?

3. How many minutes did you spend just watching TV or listening to music?

4. At what time did you go to bed? (Record as the number of minutes past 8 P.M.)

5. How many academic classes do you have?

Step 2   Conjecture with your group about the strengths of correlations between pairs of variables. For example, you may decide that the number of minutes of homework is strongly correlated with the number of academic classes. Consider each of the ten pairs of variables and identify which combinations you believe will have

  i. A positive correlation (as one increases, the other tends to increase).

  ii. A negative correlation (as one increases, the other tends to decrease).

  iii. A weak correlation.

Step 3   Gather data from each student in your class. Then enter the data into five calculator lists. Plot points for each pair of lists, and find the correlation coefficients. [▶▣ See **Calculator Note 11E** to learn how to find the correlation coefficient.◀] You may want to divide this work among members of your group. Describe the relationship between the appearance of the graph and the value of the correlation coefficient.

Step 4   Write a paragraph describing the correlations you discover. Include any pairs that are not correlated that you find surprising. You have collected a small and not very random sample; do you think these relationships would still be present if you collected answers from a random sample of your entire school population?

Name _____ **Period** _____ **Date** _____

You will need: the worksheet Looking for Connections
Sample Data

Step 1 Students working in a group created the sample survey questions here.

    1. How many minutes of homework did you do last night?

    2. How many minutes did you spend talking, calling, e-mailing, or writing to friends?

    3. How many minutes did you spend just watching TV or listening to music?

    4. At what time did you go to bed? (the number of minutes past 8 P.M.)

    5. How many academic classes do you have?

Step 2 Conjecture with your group about the strengths of correlations between pairs of variables. For example, you may decide that the number of minutes of homework is strongly correlated with the number of academic classes. Consider each of the ten pairs of variables and identify which combinations you believe will have

    i. A positive correlation (as one increases, the other tends to increase).

    ii. A negative correlation (as one increases, the other tends to decrease).

    iii. A weak correlation.

Step 3   The data gathered by the group members from all students in the class is recorded in the Looking for Connections Sample Data worksheet. Enter the data for the questions into five calculator lists. Plot points for each pair of lists, and find the correlation coefficients. [▶🖳 See **Calculator Note 11E** to learn how to find the correlation coefficient.◀] You may want to divide this work among members of your group. Describe the relationship between the appearance of the graph and the value of the correlation coefficient.

Step 4   Write a paragraph describing the correlations you discover. Include any pairs that are not correlated that you find surprising. You have collected a small and not very random sample; do you think these relationships would still be present if you collected answers from a random sample of your entire school population?

Discovering Advanced Algebra Investigation Worksheets
©2010 Key Curriculum Press

Investigation • Spin Time

Name _____ Period _____ Date _____

You will need: four different-size coins, a stopwatch or watch with a second hand

You will conduct an experiment to determine if the spin time of a coin can be explained by some attribute of the coin. Record your data in the table.

Step 1 Two important characteristics of good experimental design are **randomization** and **replication.** You'll build in randomization by spinning the coins in a random order. To ensure replication, the same spinner and timer will perform the experiment four times on each coin. Follow the Procedure Note to collect data on four coins.

Coin type	Spin time (s)

> **Procedure Note**
> 1. Assign one student to be a spinner and one student to be a timer.
> 2. Randomize the order of the coins. You can shake them up or use a random-number generator to assign the order.
> 3. Spin and time each coin once. Record the amount of time the coin spins before it comes to a complete stop.
> 4. Repeat Steps 2 and 3 so that each coin is spun four times. The order in which the four coins are spun should not be the same in every round.

Investigation • Spin Time (continued)

Step 2   What affects how long different coins spin? Is it the diameter of the coin? The weight? You'll test several characteristics to see whether they make a good predictor for spin time. For each coin, refer to the diameter, weight, and thickness, and calculate the area of the face and the volume of the coin. The table shows information about each type of coin.

Denomination	Cent	Nickel	Dime	Quarter	Half Dollar	Presidential $1	Golden Dollar
Weight	2.500 g	5.000 g	2.268 g	5.670 g	11.340 g	8.1 g	8.1 g
Diameter	0.750 in. 19.05 mm	0.835 in. 21.21 mm	0.705 in. 17.91 mm	0.955 in. 24.26 mm	1.205 in. 30.61 mm	1.043 in. 26.50 mm	1.043 in. 26.50 mm
Thickness	1.55 mm	1.95 mm	1.35 mm	1.75 mm	2.15 mm	2.00 mm	2.00 mm
Edge	Plain	Plain	Reeded	Reeded	Reeded	Edge-Lettering	Plain
Area of face							
Volume							

(*www.usmint.gov*)

Step 3   For each of the five possible predictors, calculate the coefficient of correlation and the equation of the least squares line for spin time versus that predictor. Which of these characteristics is the best linear predictor?

Step 4   A Golden Dollar weighs 8.1 g. It has a diameter of 26.50 mm and a thickness of 2.00 mm, so the area of its face is about 552 mm^2 and its volume is about 1100 mm^3. What would you estimate to be the average spin time of a Golden Dollar?

Step 5   With your group, discuss and answer these questions.

   a. What is the purpose of replication? (Why spin the same coin more than one time?)

   b. What is the purpose of randomization? (Why not spin the coins in a predetermined order?)

   c. Why use only one spinner and one timer instead of giving everyone a turn at each job?

   d. What did you consider when choosing the "best" linear predictor?

e. Suppose you did an observational study and saw that one student could spin a quarter longer than another student could spin a dime. What conclusion could you reach? What is the advantage of doing a well-designed experiment rather than an observational study?

Investigation • Spin Time

Name _____ Period _____ Date _____

You will conduct an experiment to determine if the spin time of a coin can be explained by some attribute of the coin.

Step 1 Two important characteristics of good experimental design are **randomization** and **replication.** This experiment built in randomization by spinning the coins in a random order. To ensure replication, the same spinner and timer performed the experiment four times on each coin. Data was collected on four coins by following the Procedure Note. The data were sorted by coin type and recorded in the table.

Coin type	Spin time (s)
Quarter	10.69
Quarter	12.26
Quarter	13.56
Quarter	9.71
Dime	8.38
Dime	7.47
Dime	8.87
Dime	7.37
Nickel	15.48
Nickel	13.88
Nickel	12.19
Nickel	12.54
Cent	9.6
Cent	11.39
Cent	8.25
Cent	6.78

> ### Procedure Note
>
> 1. Assign one student to be a spinner and one student to be a timer.
> 2. Randomize the order of the coins. You can shake them up or use a random-number generator to assign the order.
> 3. Spin and time each coin once. Record the amount of time the coin spins before it comes to a complete stop.
> 4. Repeat Steps 2 and 3 so that each coin is spun four times. The order in which the four coins are spun should not be the same in every round.

Step 2   What affects how long different coins spin? Is it the diameter of the
coin? The weight? You'll test several characteristics to see whether
they make a good predictor for spin time. For each coin, refer to
the diameter, weight, and thickness, and calculate the area of the
face and the volume of the coin. The table shows information
about each type of coin.

Denomination	Cent	Nickel	Dime	Quarter	Half Dollar	Presidential $1	Golden Dollar
Weight	2.500 g	5.000 g	2.268 g	5.670 g	11.340 g	8.1 g	8.1 g
Diameter	0.750 in. 19.05 mm	0.835 in. 21.21 mm	0.705 in. 17.91 mm	0.955 in. 24.26 mm	1.205 in. 30.61 mm	1.043 in. 26.50 mm	1.043 in. 26.50 mm
Thickness	1.55 mm	1.95 mm	1.35 mm	1.75 mm	2.15 mm	2.00 mm	2.00 mm
Edge	Plain	Plain	Reeded	Reeded	Reeded	Edge-Lettering	Plain
Area of face							
Volume							

(*www.usmint.gov*)

Step 3   For each of the five possible predictors, calculate the coefficient of
correlation and the equation of the least squares line for spin time
versus that predictor. Which of these characteristics is the best
linear predictor?

Step 4   A Golden Dollar weighs 8.1 g. It has a diameter of 26.50 mm
and a thickness of 2.00 mm, so the surface area of its face is about
552 mm^2 and its volume is about 1100 mm^3. What would
you estimate to be the average spin time of a Golden Dollar?

Step 5   With your group, discuss and answer these questions.

   a. What is the purpose of replication? (Why spin the same coin
   more than one time?)

   b. What is the purpose of randomization? (Why not spin the coins
   in a predetermined order?)

   c. Why use only one spinner and one timer instead of giving
   everyone a turn at each job?

   d. What did you consider when choosing the "best" linear
   predictor?

e. Suppose you did an observational study and saw that one student could spin a quarter longer than another student could spin a dime. What conclusion could you reach? What is the advantage of doing a well-designed experiment rather than an observational study?

Investigation • Similar Right Triangles

Supplemental

Name _____ **Period** _____ **Date** _____

You will need: a protractor

In this investigation you will learn more about how to define the trigonometric ratios. Each group member should independently complete Steps 1 to 4. In Step 5, you'll share your results.

Step 1   Draw an acute angle. Label it A. Use your protractor to measure the angle to the nearest degree. Be sure that each group member works with a different angle measure.

Step 2   Choose one side of your angle and draw at least three segments perpendicular to it, to create several overlapping right triangles. If necessary, extend the rays of your angle. You may recall from geometry that these right triangles are similar because their corresponding angles are congruent. As shown in this diagram, label the legs of the smallest triangle a and b, and label the hypotenuse c. As you study each of the different-size triangles, continue to let a and b represent the legs and c represent the hypotenuse.

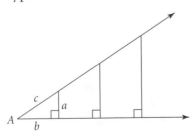

Step 3 In the table record lengths *a*, *b*, and *c* for each of your triangles. Measure to the nearest tenth of a centimeter. Then compute the ratios $\frac{a}{c}$, $\frac{b}{c}$, and $\frac{a}{b}$ to the nearest hundredth.

	a	*b*	*c*	$\frac{a}{c}$	$\frac{b}{c}$	$\frac{a}{b}$
Triangle 1						
Triangle 2						
Triangle 3						

Step 4 Set your calculator to Degree mode. Find the values of sin *A*, cos *A*, and tan *A*, where *A* is the degree measure of your angle. Round each value to the nearest hundredth. Look for relationships between the values in your table and the values of sin *A*, cos *A*, and tan *A*.

A = _____   sin *A* = _____   cos *A* = _____   tan *A* = _____

Step 5 Share your results with other group members. Carefully describe any relationships you think might be true.

Discovering Advanced Algebra Investigation Worksheets
©2010 Key Curriculum Press

Investigation • Steep Steps

Name_____   Period_____   Date_____

Have you ever noticed that some sets of steps are steeper than others? Building codes and regulations place restrictions on how steep steps can be. Over time these codes change, so stairs built in different locations and at different times may vary quite a bit in their steepness.

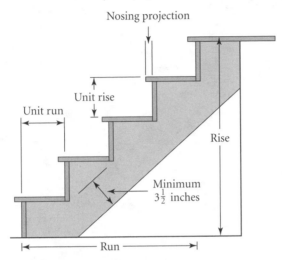

(*www.sizes.com/home/stairs.htm*)

Step 1   Refer to the diagram of stairs. According to the 1996 Council of American Building Officials and the 2000 International Code Council, the unit run should be not less than 10 inches, and the unit rise should not be more than 7.75 inches. With these limiting dimensions, what is the angle of inclination for the stairs?

Step 2   A rule of thumb for designing stairs is that the sum of the unit rise and unit run should be about 17.5 inches. Design three different sets of stairs that meet this condition. Make two of your designs within the approved building code given in Step 1. The third design should not meet the building code. Find the angle of inclination for each set of stairs.

Step 3   Consider designing steps to be built alongside Baldwin Street, Dunedin, at an angle of 20.8°.

   a. How many designs are possible? Do all possible designs meet the code given in Step 1?

b. Create a design for the steps that meets the code. Does your design meet the rule of thumb in Step 2? If not, create a new design in which the sum of the rise and run is 17.5 in.

Step 4 Wheelchair ramps are supposed to have a slope between $\frac{1}{16}$ and $\frac{1}{20}$. For each of these slopes, design a ramp to get up to a door 24 inches above the surrounding ground. What is the angle of each ramp?
(*www.mobility-advisor.com/wheelchair-ramp-specs.html*)

Investigation • Oblique Triangles

Name_____ Period_____ Date_____

You will need: a ruler, a protractor

In this investigation you'll explore a special relationship between the sines of the angle measures of an oblique triangle and the lengths of the sides.

Step 1 Have each group member draw a different acute triangle ABC. Label the length of the side opposite $\angle A$ as a, the length of the side opposite $\angle B$ as b, and the length of the side opposite $\angle C$ as c. Draw the altitude from $\angle A$ to $\overline{BC}$. Label the height h.

Step 2 The altitude divides the original triangle into two right triangles, one containing $\angle B$ and the other containing $\angle C$. Use your knowledge of right triangle trigonometry to write an expression involving $\sin B$ and h, and an expression with $\sin C$ and h. Combine the two expressions by eliminating h. Write your new expression as a proportion in the form

$$\frac{\sin B}{?} = \frac{\sin C}{?}$$

Discovering Advanced Algebra Investigation Worksheets
©2010 Key Curriculum Press

Investigation • Oblique Triangles (continued)

Step 3 Now draw the altitude from $\angle B$ to $\overline{AC}$ and label the height j. Repeat Step 2 using expressions involving j, $\sin C$, and $\sin A$. What proportion do you get when you eliminate j?

Step 4 Compare the proportions that you wrote in Steps 2 and 3. Use the transitive property of equality to combine them into an extended proportion:

$$\frac{?}{?} = \frac{?}{?} = \frac{?}{?}$$

Step 5 Share your results with the members of your group. Did everyone get the same proportion in Step 4?

Sine, cosine, and tangent are defined for all real angle measures. Therefore, you can find the sine of obtuse angles as well as the sines of acute angles and right angles. Does your work from Steps 1–5 hold true for obtuse triangles as well? (In Lesson 12.4, you will learn how these definitions are extended beyond right triangles.)

Step 6 Have each group member draw a different obtuse triangle. Measure the angles and the sides of your triangle. Substitute the measurements and evaluate to verify that the proportion from Step 4 holds true for your obtuse triangles as well.

Investigation • Around the Corner

Name_____ **Period**_____ **Date**_____

You will need: metersticks or a tape measure,
a protractor

The towns of Easton and Westville lie on opposite sides of a mountain. The townspeople wish to have a tunnel connecting the towns constructed through the mountain. A construction engineer positions herself so that she can see both towns. She plans to make some measurements and use trigonometry to determine the length of the proposed tunnel.

In this investigation you will simulate this situation. Position three members of your group so that two people are on opposite sides of a wall and the third person can see both of them. The first two group members represent the two towns, and the wall represents the mountain. The third member represents the engineer.

Find the distance between the two towns. Sketch an overhead view of the situation, show the measurements you make, and show your calculations.

Discovering Advanced Algebra Investigation Worksheets
©2010 Key Curriculum Press

Investigation • Extending Trigonometric Functions

Name _____ Period _____ Date _____

You will need: a protractor

In this investigation you'll learn how to calculate the sine, cosine, and tangent of non-acute angles on the coordinate plane.

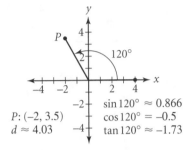

P: $(-2, 3.5)$
$d \approx 4.03$

$\sin 120° \approx 0.866$
$\cos 120° = -0.5$
$\tan 120° \approx -1.73$

> ## Procedure Note
>
> 1. Draw a point on the positive x-axis. Rotate the point counterclockwise about the origin by the given angle measure and draw the image point. (If the angle measure is negative, rotate clockwise.) Then connect the image point to the origin. The angle between the segment and the positive x-axis, in the direction of rotation, represents the amount of rotation.
> 2. Use your calculator to find the sine, cosine, and tangent of this angle.
> 3. Estimate the coordinates of the rotated point.
> 4. Use the distance formula to find the length of the segment.

Step 1 Follow the Procedure Note for each angle measure given below. An example is shown for 120°.

    a. 135°

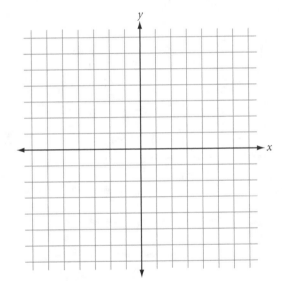

b. 210°

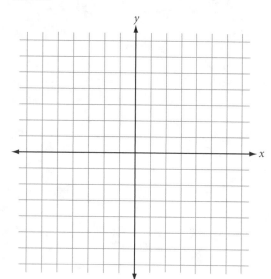

c. 270°

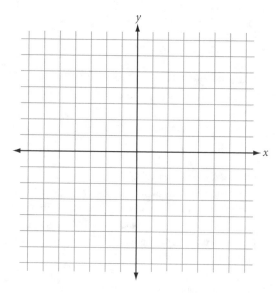

d. 320°

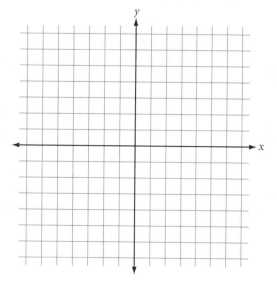

e. −100°

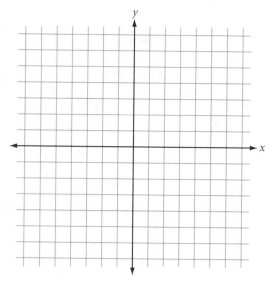

Step 2   Experiment with the estimated *x*- and *y*-coordinates and the segment length to find a way to calculate the sine, cosine, and tangent. (Your values are all estimates, so just try to get close.)

Step 3   Plot the point $(-3, 1)$ and draw a segment from it to the origin. Label as *A* the angle between the segment and the positive *x*-axis. Use your method from Step 2 to find the values of sin *A*, cos *A*, and tan *A*. What happens when you try using the inverse $\sin^{-1}$ to find the value of *A*? What happens for $\cos^{-1}$ and $\tan^{-1}$?

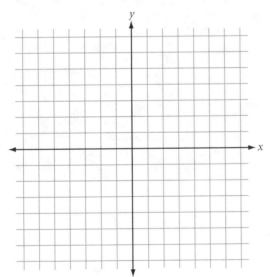

Step 4 Now consider the general case of the angle θ between the positive x-axis and a segment connecting the origin to the point (x, y). Give definitions for the values of $\sin \theta$, $\cos \theta$, and $\tan \theta$.

Investigation • Vector Addition and Subtraction

Name _____   **Period** _____   **Date** _____

You will use these vectors in this investigation.

$\mathbf{a} = \langle 2, 3 \rangle$ $\mathbf{b} = \langle 4, 1 \rangle$ $\mathbf{d} = \langle -3, 2 \rangle$ $\mathbf{e} = \langle 3, -1 \rangle$ $\mathbf{f} = \langle -1, -2 \rangle$

Step 1   On the grid, draw the vector $\mathbf{a} = \langle 2, 3 \rangle$. Remember to draw an arrowhead at the head, or tip, of the vector.

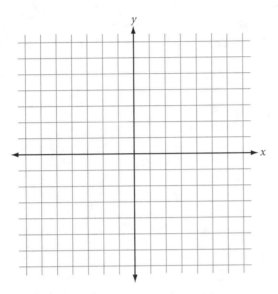

Step 2   Add the vector $\mathbf{b} = \langle 4, 1 \rangle$ to $\mathbf{a}$. Draw $\mathbf{b}$ so that the tail of $\mathbf{b}$ starts at the tip of $\mathbf{a}$. The tip of $\mathbf{b}$ should be 4 units to the right and 1 unit up from its tail. Don't forget the arrowhead at the tip.

Step 3   Draw the sum, or resultant vector, $\mathbf{c}$. What is its rectangular form?

Step 4   Repeat Steps 1–3 to complete these vector sums:

i. b + a

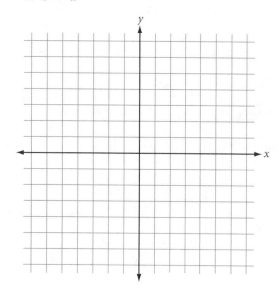

ii. d + e

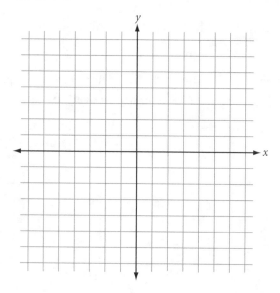

iii. b + f

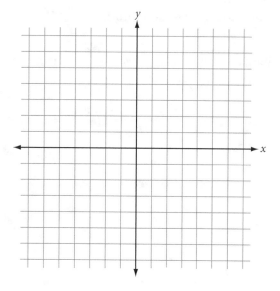

iv. a + e

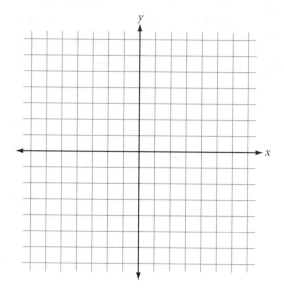

Discovering Advanced Algebra Investigation Worksheets
©2010 Key Curriculum Press

Step 5   Look at the rectangular form of the resultant vectors. Complete the following definition of vector addition for vectors in rectangular form.

If $\mathbf{a} = \langle a_1, a_2 \rangle$ and $\mathbf{b} = \langle b_1, b_2 \rangle$, then the sum $\mathbf{a} + \mathbf{b}$ is $\langle a_1, a_2 \rangle + \langle b_1, b_2 \rangle = \langle$ _____ , _____ $\rangle$.

Step 6   Subtracting a number is the same as adding its opposite. It's the same for vectors. The opposite of vector $\mathbf{b}$ is called $-\mathbf{b}$. It has the same magnitude as $\mathbf{b}$, but it points in the opposite direction. The difference $\mathbf{a} - \mathbf{b}$ is the same as the sum $\mathbf{a} + -\mathbf{b}$.

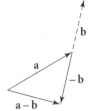

Draw a representation of each difference.

i. a − b

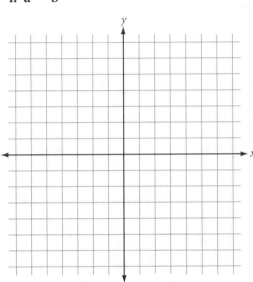

ii. b − a

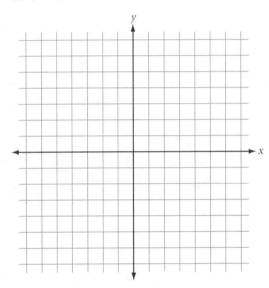

iii. d − e

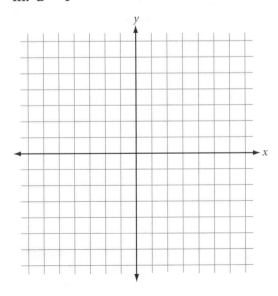

iv. e − f

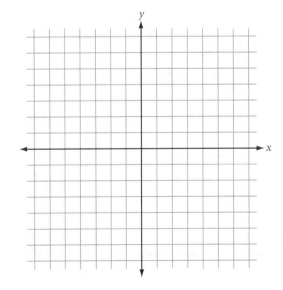

Step 7   Based on your drawings, complete the following definition
of vector subtraction for vectors in rectangular form.

If $\mathbf{a} = \langle a_1, a_2 \rangle$ and $\mathbf{b} = \langle b_1, b_2 \rangle$, then the difference $\mathbf{a} - \mathbf{b}$ is
$\langle a_1, a_2 \rangle - \langle b_1, b_2 \rangle = \langle$ _____ , _____ $\rangle$.

Step 8   Create a conjecture about multiplying a vector by a scalar
(number). For example, what would it mean to multiply $2 \cdot \mathbf{a}$?
(*Hint:* This is the same as adding $\mathbf{a} + \mathbf{a}$.) Complete the following
definition of scalar multiplication.

If $\mathbf{a} = \langle a_1, a_2 \rangle$ and k is a scalar, then the product $k \cdot \mathbf{a}$ is
$k \cdot \langle a_1, a_2 \rangle = \langle$ _____ , _____ $\rangle$.

Step 9   The magnitude (length) of a vector is symbolized placing the vector
name inside vertical bars, like an absolute-value sign. Find the
magnitudes of $\mathbf{a}$ and $\mathbf{b}$, then complete the following definition
of the magnitude of a vector in rectangular form.

If $\mathbf{a} = \langle a_1, a_2 \rangle$ then the magnitude of
$\mathbf{a}$, $|\mathbf{a}|$ is _____ .

Investigation • Parametric Walk

Name _____ **Period** _____ **Date** _____

You will need: two motion sensors, masking tape

This investigation involves four participants: a walker, recorder X, recorder Y, and a director.

> ## Procedure Note
>
> 1. The walker starts at one end of the segment and walks slowly for 5 s to reach the other end.
> 2. Recorder X points a motion sensor set for 5 s at the walker and moves along the *y*-axis, keeping even with the walker, thus measuring the *x*-coordinate of the walker's path as a function of time.
> 3. Simultaneously, recorder Y points a motion sensor set for 5 s at the walker and moves along the *x*-axis, keeping even with the walker, thus measuring the *y*-coordinate of the walker's path as a function of time.
> 4. The director starts all three participants at the same moment and counts out the seconds.

Step 1   Mark the first quadrant of a coordinate graph on the floor with tape. Identify the *x*- and *y*-axes and mark a segment, as in the diagram at right. Draw the segment on the grid below.

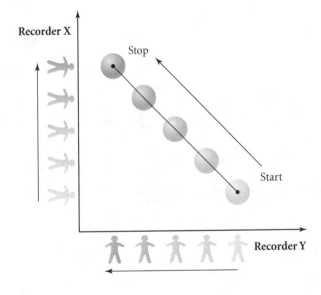

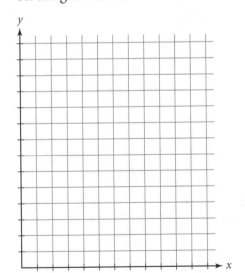

Step 2   Perform the activity as described in the Procedure Note.
[▶ 🖳 See **Calculator Note 12E** for additional instructions on how to set up your motion sensors.◀]

Step 3   Find a function in the form $x = f(t)$ that fits the data from X's motion sensor.

Step 4   Find a function in the form $y = g(t)$ that fits the data from Y's motion sensor.

Step 5   On a third calculator, transfer the distance values from X's motion sensor into list *xdist* and the distance values from Y's motion sensor into list *ydist*. Plot these data as ordered pairs (*xdist, ydist*) along with the parametric functions $x = f(t)$ and $y = g(t)$. How do they compare?

Step 6   Solve $x = f(t)$ for t and substitute this expression for t into $y = g(t)$.

Step 7   Graph your solution to Step 6 with the (*xdist, ydist*) data.
[▶ 🖳 See **Calculator Note 12F** to learn about graphing functions while still in Parametric mode. ◀]

Investigation • Parametric Walk (continued)

Step 8   Based on this investigation, explain what eliminating the parameter does to parametric equations.

Name_____ Period_____ Date_____

This investigation involves four participants: a walker, recorder X, recorder Y, and a director.

> ### Procedure Note
>
> 1. The walker starts at one end of the segment and walks slowly for 5 s to reach the other end.
> 2. Recorder X points a motion sensor set for 5 s at the walker and moves along the *y*-axis, keeping even with the walker, thus measuring the *x*-coordinate of the walker's path as a function of time.
> 3. Simultaneously, recorder Y points a motion sensor set for 5 s at the walker and moves along the *x*-axis, keeping even with the walker, thus measuring the *y*-coordinate of the walker's path as a function of time.
> 4. The director starts all three participants at the same moment and counts out the seconds.

Step 1 Students set up their classroom for this investigation. Using masking tape, they marked the first quadrant of a coordinate graph on the floor. Then they marked a segment with the tape, as in the diagram at right.

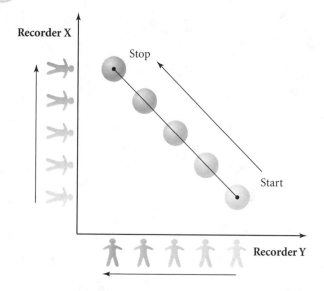

Discovering Advanced Algebra Investigation Worksheets
©2010 Key Curriculum Press

Step 2   Four students then performed the activity as described in the Procedure Note. This table contains representative data values from the complete data set they collected. t is the time in seconds, x is the x-coordinate of the walker's path collected by Recorder X, and y is the y-coordinate of the walker's path collected by Recorder Y.

t	x	y
0.1	1.78	1.95
0.6	1.71	2.02
1.1	1.62	2.11
1.6	1.50	2.12
2.1	1.43	2.21
2.6	1.36	2.25
3.1	1.26	2.32
3.6	1.19	2.38
4.1	1.10	2.39
4.6	1.00	2.47
5.0	0.95	2.50

Step 3   Find a function in the form $x = f(t)$ that fits the data from X's motion sensor.

Step 4   Find a function in the form $y = g(t)$ that fits the data from Y's motion sensor.

Step 5   On your calculator, transfer the distance values from X's motion sensor into list *xdist* and the distance values from Y's motion sensor into list *ydist*. Plot these data as ordered pairs (*xdist*, *ydist*) along with the parametric functions $x = f(t)$ and $y = g(t)$. How do they compare?

Step 6   Solve $x = f(t)$ for t and substitute this expression for t into
            $y = g(t)$.

Step 7   Graph your solution to Step 6 with the (*xdist, ydist*) data.
            [▶️🖥 See **Calculator Note 12F** to learn about graphing functions while still in
            Parametric mode.◀]

Step 8   Based on this investigation, explain what eliminating the parameter
            does to parametric equations.

Investigation • Paddle Wheel

Name _____ **Period** _____ **Date** _____

While swimming along, a frog reaches out and grabs onto the rim of a paddle wheel with radius 1 m. The center of the wheel is at water level. The frog, clinging tightly to the wheel, is immediately lifted from the surface of the river.

Step 1 The wheel spins counterclockwise at a rate of one rotation every 6 minutes. Through how many degrees does the frog rotate each minute? Each second?

Step 2 Create three lists on your calculator. Name the first list *time* and fill it with the values {0, 15, 30, 45, . . . , 900}. Name the second list *hpos* and define it as *hpos* = cos(*time*). Name the third list *vpos* and define it as *vpos* = sin(*time*). Make a scatter plot of (*hpos*, *vpos*) in a square window and trace the path of the frog. Sketch the plot on the grid below.

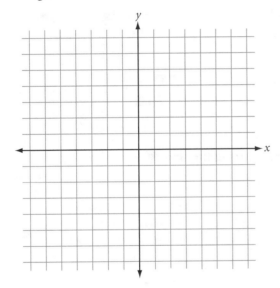

Step 3   Explain how to find the *x*- and *y*-coordinates of any point on the circle. In this context, what is the meaning of those points? What might be more appropriate names for lists *hpos* and *vpos*?

Step 4   Scroll down your lists and describe any patterns you see.

Step 5   Use your lists to answer these questions.

    a. What is the frog's location after 1215°, or 1215 s? When, during the first three rotations of the wheel, is the frog at that same location?

    b. When is the frog at a height of −0.5 m during the first three rotations?

    c. What are the maximum and minimum *x*- and *y*-values?

Step 6 Make scatter plots of (*time, hpos*) and (*time, vpos*) on the same screen, using a different symbol for each plot. Use the domain $0 \text{ s} \leq time \leq 360 \text{ s}$. How do the graphs compare? How can you use the graphs to find the frog's position at any time? Why do you think the sine and cosine functions are sometimes called circular functions?

Investigation • A Radian Protractor

Name_____ **Period**_____ **Date**_____

You will need: string, the worksheet A Radian Protractor

Use the semicircle on the worksheet to complete the investigation.

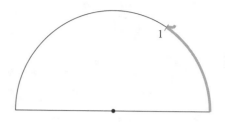

Step 1   Mark the length of the radius of the semicircle on your string.

Step 2   Starting from the right-hand base, use the radius length of string to measure off an arc whose length is the same as the radius.

Step 3   The central angle intercepting this arc has a measure of **1 radian.** Use your radius length of string to mark points that correspond to angles with measures of 2 and 3 radians.

Step 4   Fold your radius length of string in half and use this length to locate points corresponding to angles with measures 0.5, 1.5, and 2.5 radians.

Step 5   If the radius of your circle is *r*, calculate the length of a semicircular arc. How many radians is this? Mark this radian value on your protractor.

Step 6   What is the length of the arc intercepted by a right angle? How many radians are associated with a right angle? Mark this radian value on your protractor.

Step 7   Find radian values that correspond with these common angle measurements and mark them on your protractor: 30°, 45°, 60°, 120°, 135°, and 150°.

Discovering Advanced Algebra Investigation Worksheets
©2010 Key Curriculum Press

Investigation • The Pendulum II

Name _____   **Period** _____   **Date** _____

You will need: a washer, string, a motion sensor

Suspend a washer from two strings so that it hangs 10 to 15 cm from the floor between two tables or desks. Place the motion sensor on the floor about 1 m in front of the washer hanging at rest. Pull the washer back about 20 to 30 cm and let it swing. Collect data points for 2 s of time. Model your data with both a sine function and a cosine function. Give real-world meanings for all numerical values in each equation.

Investigation • The Pendulum II

With Sample Data

Name_____ Period_____ Date_____

A group of students used a motion sensor and followed these directions to collect data for the investigation.

Suspend a washer from two strings so that it hangs 10 to 15 cm from the floor between two tables or desks. Place the motion sensor on the floor about 1 m in front of the washer hanging at rest. Pull the washer back about 20 to 30 cm and let it swing.

They collected data points for 2 s. Their results are recorded in the tables.

Time (s)	Distance (m)
0.05	0.900
0.10	0.903
0.15	0.899
0.20	0.888
0.25	0.873
0.30	0.855
0.35	0.836
0.40	0.814
0.45	0.791
0.50	0.768

Time (s)	Distance (m)
0.55	0.749
0.60	0.730
0.65	0.714
0.70	0.704
0.75	0.698
0.80	0.697
0.85	0.702
0.90	0.712
0.95	0.727
1.00	0.745

Discovering Advanced Algebra Investigation Worksheets
©2010 Key Curriculum Press

Time (s)	Distance (m)
1.05	0.766
1.10	0.786
1.15	0.809
1.20	0.830
1.25	0.850
1.30	0.867
1.35	0.881
1.40	0.891
1.45	0.894
1.50	0.884

Time (s)	Distance (m)
1.55	0.889
1.60	0.879
1.65	0.863
1.70	0.844
1.75	0.824
1.80	0.802
1.85	0.779
1.90	0.760
1.95	0.740
2.00	0.724

Enter the data in two lists in your calculator, and graph it. Then model the data with both a sine function and a cosine function. Give real-world meanings for all numerical values in each equation.

Investigation • Exploring the Inverses

Name_____ **Period**_____ **Date**_____

In this investigation you will explore the graphs of trigonometric functions and their inverses.

Step 1   On the graph grid, create *x*- and *y*-axes ranging from −10 to 10. Mark both axes from −10 to 10 at intervals of 1 unit. Then mark the values of π, 2π, and 3π on each axis. Use the same scale for both axes. That is, the distance from 0 to π on your *y*-axis should be the same as the distance from 0 to π on your *x*-axis. Carefully graph $y = \sin x$. Test a few points on your graph to make sure they fit the sine function.

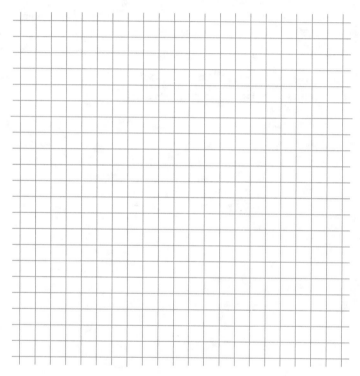

Step 2   Add the line $y = x$ to your graph. Fold your paper along this line and then trace the image of $y = \sin x$ onto your paper.

Verify that this transformation maps the point $\left(\frac{\pi}{2}, 1\right)$ onto $\left(1, \frac{\pi}{2}\right)$, $(\pi, 0)$ onto $(0, \pi)$, and $\left(\frac{3\pi}{2}, -1\right)$ onto $\left(-1, \frac{3\pi}{2}\right)$.

In general, every point (x, y) should map onto (y, x).

Step 3   If your original graph is $y = \sin x$, then the equation of the inverse, when *x* and *y* are switched, is $x = \sin y$. Is the inverse of $y = \sin x$ a function? Why or why not?

Discovering Advanced Algebra Investigation Worksheets
©2010 Key Curriculum Press

Step 4   Darken the portion of the curve $x = \sin y$ between $y = -\frac{\pi}{2}$ and $y = \frac{\pi}{2}$. Is this portion of the graph a function? Why or why not?

Step 5   Carefully sketch graphs of $y = \cos x$ and its inverse, $x = \cos y$, on these axes. Then darken a portion of the curve $x = \cos y$ that is a function. What interval did you select for y?

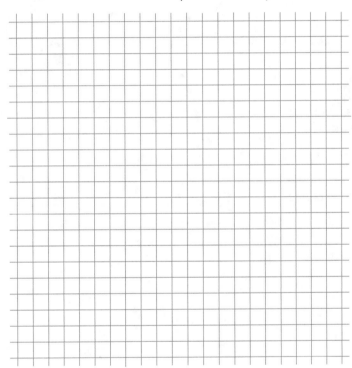

Investigation • A Bouncing Spring

Name_____ Period_____ Date_____

You will need: a motion sensor, a spring, a mass of
50 to 100 g, a support stand

In this experiment you will suspend a mass from a spring. When you pull
down on the mass slightly, and release, the mass will move up and down.
In reality, the amount of motion gradually decreases, and eventually the
mass returns to rest. However, if the initial motion is small, then the
decrease in the motion occurs more slowly and can be ignored during
the first few seconds.

> ## Procedure Note
>
> 1. Attach a mass to the bottom of a spring. Position the motion sensor
>   directly below the spring, leaving space to pull down on the mass.
> 2. Set the motion sensor to collect about 5 s of data. Pull the mass
>   down slightly, and release at the same moment as you begin
>   gathering data.

Step 1 Follow the Procedure Note to collect data on the height of the
bouncing spring for a few seconds.

Step 2 Delete values from your lists to limit your data to about four cycles.
Identify the phase shift, amplitude, period, frequency, and vertical
shift of your function.

Step 3 Write a sine or cosine function that models the data.

Discovering Advanced Algebra Investigation Worksheets
©2010 Key Curriculum Press

Investigation • A Bouncing Spring (continued)

Step 4 Answer these questions, based on your equation and your observations.

    a. How does each of the numbers in your equation from Step 3 correspond to the motion of the spring?

    b. How would your equation change if you moved the motion sensor 1 m farther away?

    c. How would your equation change if you pulled the spring slightly lower when you started?

Investigation • A Bouncing Spring

Name_____ **Period**_____ **Date**_____

You will need: the worksheet Bouncing Spring Sample Data

In this experiment a mass was suspended from a spring. A student pulled the mass down slightly and released, and the mass then moved up and down. In reality, the amount of motion gradually decreased, and eventually the mass returned to rest. However, if the initial motion is small, then the decrease in the motion occurs more slowly and can be ignored during the first few seconds.

> *Procedure Note*
>
> 1. Attach a mass to the bottom of a spring. Position the motion sensor directly below the spring, leaving space to pull down on the mass.
> 2. Set the motion sensor to collect about 5 s of data. Pull the mass down slightly, and release at the same moment as you begin gathering data.

Step 1 A group of students followed the Procedure Note to collect data on the height of the bouncing spring for a few seconds.

Step 2 The students deleted values from their lists to limit the data to about four cycles. These data are recorded in the table on the worksheet Bouncing Spring Sample Data. Add these data values to two lists in your calculator and graph them. Identify the phase shift, amplitude, period, frequency, and vertical shift of your function.

Discovering Advanced Algebra Investigation Worksheets
©2010 Key Curriculum Press

Step 3   Write a sine or cosine function that models the data.

Step 4   Answer these questions, based on your equation and your observations.

   a. How does each of the numbers in your equation from Step 3 correspond to the motion of the spring?

   b. How would your equation change if the motion sensor was moved 1 m farther away?

   c. How would your equation change if the spring was pulled slightly lower when it started in the investigation?

Investigation • Pythagorean Identities

Name_____   Period_____   Date_____

Step 1   Use your calculator to graph the equation $y = \sin^2 x + \cos^2 x$. (You'll probably have to enter this as $y = (\sin x)^2 + (\cos x)^2$.) Does this graph look familiar? Use your graph to write an identity.

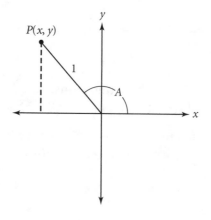

Step 2   Use the definitions for sin A, cos A, and the diagram at right to prove your identity.

Step 3   Explain why you think this identity is called a Pythagorean identity.

Step 4   Solve the identity from Step 1 for $\cos^2 x$ to get another identity. Then solve for $\sin^2 x$ to get another variation.

$\cos^2 x =$ _____

$\sin^2 x =$ _____

Discovering Advanced Algebra Investigation Worksheets
©2010 Key Curriculum Press

Investigation • Pythagorean Identities (continued)

Step 5   Divide both sides of the identity from Step 1 by $\cos^2 x$ to develop a new identity. Simplify so that there are no trigonometric functions in the denominator.

Step 6   Verify your identity from Step 5 with a graph or table. Name any domain values for which the identity is undefined.

Step 7   Divide both sides of the identity from Step 1 by $\sin^2 x$ to develop a new identity. Simplify so that there are no trigonometric functions in the denominator.

Step 8   Verify the identity from Step 7 with a graph. Name any domain values for which the identity is undefined.

Investigation • Sound Wave

Name_____ **Period**_____ **Date**_____

You will need: a microphone probe, two tuning forks,
musical instrument, *(optional)*

In this investigation you'll explore the frequency of some tones and combinations of tones.

Step 1 Choose a tuning fork and collect data as described in the Procedure Note. Find an equation to fit the data. Repeat this process with a second tuning fork.

> ### Procedure Note
>
> 1. Set up your calculator and microphone probe to collect sound frequency data. [▶☐ See **Calculator Note 13D.**◀]
> 2. To ring a tuning fork, rap it sharply on a semisoft surface like a book or the heel of your shoe. Hold the fork close to the microphone and begin collecting data. When you use more than one fork, be sure to hold them equidistant from the microphone.

Step 2 Using the same two tuning forks that you used in Step 1, ring both forks simultaneously, and collect frequency data. You should see a combination of sinusoids, rather than a simple sinusoid. Model the data with an equation that is the sum of two simple sinusoid equations.

Discovering Advanced Algebra Investigation Worksheets
©2010 Key Curriculum Press

Investigation • Sound Wave (continued)

Step 3 Select a musical instrument, perhaps a flute, violin, piano, timpani, or your voice. Play one note (or string) and collect data. You should see a complex wave, probably too complex for you to write an equation. Identify the fundamental frequency. See if you can identify the frequencies of some of the overtones as well.

Investigation • Sound Wave   With Sample Data

Name_____ Period_____ Date_____

You will need: Calculator lists XTME, APRE, EPRE, AEPRE,
and RPRE

In this investigation you'll explore the frequency of some tones and
combinations of tones. The data sets collected in the investigation are
too large to easily enter by hand, so you will transfer the following lists
directly to your calculator.

> **Procedure Note**
>
> 1. Set up your calculator and
>   microphone probe to collect
>   sound frequency data.
> 2. To ring a tuning fork, rap it
>   sharply on a semisoft surface
>   like a book or the heel of your
>   shoe. Hold the fork close to
>   the microphone and begin
>   collecting data. When you
>   use more than one fork, be
>   sure to hold them equidistant
>   from the microphone.

XTME	Time (seconds)
APRE	A-440 Hz Tuning Fork (pressure)
EPRE	E-329.6 Hz Tuning Fork (pressure)
AEPRE	Combination of A and E Tuning Forks (pressure)
RPRE	Recorder (pressure)

Complete the transfers before working on the investigation.

Step 1   A group of students chose a A-440 Hz tuning fork and
collected data as described in the Procedure Note. Graph
these data, using XTME (time) as the independent variable
and APRE (the A tuning fork) as the dependent variable.
Find an equation to fit these data.

Next the students chose a E-329.6 Hz tuning fork and repeated the
process. Graph these data, using XTME (time) as the independent
variable and APRE (the A tuning fork) as the dependent variable.
Find an equation to fit these data.

Step 2   Using the same two tuning forks they used in Step 1, the students
rang both forks simultaneously, and collected frequency data.
Graph these data, using XTME (time) as the independent variable
and AEPRE (both tuning forks) as the dependent variable.

Discovering Advanced Algebra Investigation Worksheets
©2010 Key Curriculum Press

You should see a combination of sinusoids, rather than a simple sinusoid. Model the data with an equation that is the sum of two simple sinusoid equations.

Step 3   Finally, the students played one note on a recorder and collected the data. Graph these data, using XTME (time) as the independent variable and RPRE (the recorder) as the dependent variable. You should see a complex wave, probably too complex for you to write an equation. Identify the fundamental frequency. See if you can identify the frequencies of some of the overtones as well.

Key Curriculum Press
Innovators in Mathematics Education

Comment Form

Please take a moment to provide us with feedback about this book. We are eager to read any comments or suggestions you may have. Once you've filled out this form, simply fold it along the dotted lines and drop it in the mail. We'll pay the postage. Thank you!

Your Name _____

School _____

School Address _____

City/State/Zip _____

Phone _____

Book Title _____

Please list any comments you have about this book.

Do you have any suggestions for improving the student or teacher material?

To request a catalog, or place an order, call us toll free at 800-995-MATH, or send a fax to 800-541-2242. For more information, visit Key's website at www.keypress.com.

Please detach page, fold on lines and tape edge.

Key Curriculum Press
Innovators in Mathematics Education

Comment Form

Please take a moment to provide us with feedback about this book. We are eager to read any comments or suggestions you may have. Once you've filled out this form, simply fold it along the dotted lines and drop it in the mail. We'll pay the postage. Thank you!

Your Name _____

School _____

School Address _____

City/State/Zip _____

Phone _____

Book Title _____

Please list any comments you have about this book.

Do you have any suggestions for improving the student or teacher material?

To request a catalog, or place an order, call us toll free at 800-995-MATH, or send a fax to 800-541-2242.
For more information, visit Key's website at www.keypress.com.

Please detach page, fold on lines and tape edge.